LET **ERMA** DO IT

LET

ERMA DO IT

THE FULL STORY OF

AUTOMATION

BY DAVID O. WOODBURY

Harcourt, Brace and Company · New York

LIBRARY OF CONGRESS CATALOG CARD NUMBER: 56-11297

PRINTED IN THE UNITED STATES OF AMERICA

For . . .
My Own Automation Expert
I. W.

FOREWORD

An editor friend of mine has warned me that nobody reads the Foreword to a book; therefore, make it short and don't put anything important into it. There is a slight flaw in the logic of this admirable advice. If nobody reads it why put it in? But I am putting a Foreword in anyhow. Habit, probably, or a slight touch of vanity. It is pleasant to meet the reader as he looks for his slippers and glasses and turns off the TV. For that one moment the author is a person; he is on the reader's side. I once wrote a book with a high-powered introduction and nobody ever read anything *but* the introduction. I won't do that now. The editor is right; a Foreword is just a gesture, like slicking your hair before you are hung.

The title of this book is not a complete description of it. While ERMA is all automation, Automation is not all ERMA. The title symbolizes the subject, but only partially, and as inadequately as that long list of feminine names describes the hurricanes that visit the Atlantic coast. But, like the Weather Bureau, we had to call our project something, and ERMA seemed like a good bet. A girl's name is apt to catch the eye, especially on a book jacket. To find out about ERMA you will have to turn to Chapter 15, but I don't recommend it for a start. For an understanding of feminine character one should have some background; this I have attempted to put in at the beginning. Besides, a lot of automation doesn't concern ERMA at all, and this comes in during the first few chapters, too.

Automation—the word—is not in the dictionary, but that is about the only place you will not find it. Automation—the concept—is everywhere today, roaring up out of the laboratories into thousands of factories, onto the streets, into homes and offices, and out among the farms. It is something we should all know about, *must* all know about if we expect to live tomorrow. It is, in its detail, a complicated, abstruse, technical affair, proudly looked upon by the scientists as their most sophisticated endeavor to date. However, I am brash enough to believe that it can be explained.

My good friend Dr. Gordon Brown, of M.I.T., a great pioneer in automation, says that it is an "open-ended issue." His concept sets the theme of this book, and the pressure of his inspiration has greatly helped me to write it. We live in a closed-ended world, surrounded by endeavors and possessions that come to a finish and are forgotten. An open-ended issue, by contrast, is one that goes on and outward forever, like space. The more you travel towards its apparent horizons the wider they become. The more you learn of it the more you need to know. The more skillfully you use it, the greater are its future promises. This I have tried to indicate in the following pages, but they are already far behind. The achievement moves on with gathering speed, a speed far beyond the power of any scribe to match in print.

Though I wrote the book, and did its research, as fast as I was able, the picture has already changed. Some of the things you will hear about automation will not be found in ERMA —things like the magnetic amplifier recently invented by Beckman Instruments, Inc., or like "Mr. Meticulous," Bell Laboratories' new automatic gadget that can build near-perfect transistors an atom or two at a time. It might be a good idea to paste an empty envelope into the back of the book and slip into it clippings from magazines and the daily press, detailing other new things which hadn't appeared when I wrote. You would soon find that the envelope was not big enough; a filing cabinet would be needed and the book, like this Foreword, would sink to the level of an introduction. An introduction, however, which would still contain the fundamentals and the guiding spirit of the new day.

Automation is a big thing, perhaps the biggest so far in human progress. Some call it the Intellectual Revolution, a new approach to thinking, which can change us from the slaves to the masters of our material needs. After 10,000 years of struggle, we seem to have reached a point in history where there is a definite shift from muscles to minds. It is a vital point to study and understand.

There will be casualties. Some jobs will dissolve into better ones; many venerable methods will fall by the wayside to make room for more effective ones. A few people, unable to accept the new concepts, will withdraw into themselves, wistfully looking back into the past. I hope that this book will help, in a small way, to reduce the number of these.

Speaking of casualties, one of them may even be me. Recently a book was published which had been written, printed, bound and delivered entirely by a computing machine. This mechanical wizard did the whole job in less than two hours, after human brains had spent a week or two thinking up what they wanted the book to say.

This is better than I can do, even if I had a friend who would do all my thinking for me. If ERMA should find out about this and go off on a writing jag some day, I would be out of a job. Very well, I will simply invent a new ERMA that can read books, too.

DAVID O. WOODBURY

Santa Barbara, California
June, 1956

CONTENTS

1
THIS BUSINESS ABOUT AUTOMATION

1 | SIXTY-FOUR (BILLION) DOLLAR WORD

There's a story around about a lady in New Jersey who looked out of her window one afternoon some years ago and saw a U.S. Mail truck unload 746 copies of *Time* at her mailbox. Her vigorous protest to the publisher in due time caused an investigation. It seemed that an addressing machine had stuck and had banged out Smith, Smith, Smith, Smith . . . until an attendant, alerted by the unaccustomed sound, stopped it.

"We are very sorry, Madam, and the extra magazines will be removed," a hastily sent *Time* representative assured her. "But you know, you're lucky, at that. If that girl hadn't caught the error when she did, you might have got the whole edition!"

This, in a wry way, illuminates the pitfalls of an automated world. It shows what happens to the ordinary citizen who lives in the pioneering stages of a great mechanical change. A definition of automation based on an addressing machine gone wrong is hardly reliable. Yet it is as close as the public usually comes. The truth is that slogan-loving America has coined a new term and can't quite make it out. Miss Smith's confusion is our own.

What *is* automation?

The berserk addressing machine, indeed, is the very sort of calamity we are trying to get away from *with* automation. It illustrates rather well the half-baked condition of the machine

3

Pre-automation: 746 copies of Time *magazine arrive at the Smith mailbox*

age we are just leaving. Our mechanical servants have grown too complicated to behave normally on all occasions; the human brain is not quite alert enough to catch them at it in time. Fully automated addressing machines would instantly know it if their innards stuck. They would permit themselves a polite groan, perhaps, but would instantly reroute their digestive processes to correct the mistake before Miss Smith or anybody else even heard of it.

She was not the victim of automation at all, but of plain, old-fashioned automatic machinery, at best only an ancestor. The world is full of automatic machinery, but has hardly begun on automation.

What is the distinction?

Simply that automation makes mechanical devices responsible

for their own behavior. As a first approximation, the word covers a mechanical state of affairs in which machines acquire a sense of duty independent of their operators. They are capable of bringing off the *right* result as well as performing the duties necessary to achieving that result.

Being a coined word, "automation" should mean only what the fellow who coined it had in mind. Unhappily, this leads to confusion, as more than one person claims parenthood—a noteworthy variation on the usual theme of disclaiming parenthood.

The Ford Motor Company and a young Harvard Business School graduate named John Diebold thought up the term simultaneously and independently, some ten years ago. As they applied it to slightly different things, a looseness of definition began right there. Their common ground of meaning, such as it was, referred to manufacturing operations, previously dependent upon human skill, but now conducted by intricate machines with their own built-in controls. The result was to be factories producing faster, more uniform, and more accurate work at less cost. An admitted effect was that people who had formerly been needed to run the old machines were not needed to run the new, and hence lost their jobs. This was to effect great savings, provided that the new machinery did not cost so much as to eat up the savings. It is turning out that automated machines do not eat up their savings because they produce high-grade goods at enormous speed. Nor are the dislocated people going on the breadlines. They are at work in jobs of higher skill which the new robots require.

Ford, which probably had the real edge on originating "automation," said it was "the automatic handling of parts between progressive production processes." Diebold, meanwhile, called it "a new word denoting both automatic operation and the process of making things automatic." Diebold soon enlarged his definition, bolstering it with this: "The key to automation is feedback, or the controlled-loop system." It is not of much help to us, at this point, to be reminded that windmills of the seventeenth century employed feedback to keep their sails trimmed to the breeze. (We shall explore feedback frequently as we go on; it is not as confusing as it appears here.)

From which it is evident that in the beginning technical matters, clear only to engineers, clouded the definition and placed it in a scientific strait jacket.

For our purposes at the outset it is better to begin with a broader concept—one that has grown up on a wider base than that which occupies the engineers. Like Boston, automation today can be called a state of mind. It is a new pattern for industrial society, a fresh, startling, high-gear way of life, something as far-reaching as the Industrial Revolution itself. But, let it be added at once, entirely different.

As we go into this account we shall see more and more definitions develop, some technical, some sociological, some economic. Our society has reached the point where it is no longer adequate to improve the mechanics of doing things. In the past decade there has been a definite breakthrough in science, which makes it possible to endow machines with discretion, with the power of choice, and with the ability to evaluate results—attributes of the mind which only human beings possessed before. With intricate electronic sensing apparatus for measuring performance in terms of desired standards, automated machines can carry out the logical steps of a process in order, making certain that each step is done correctly before going on to the next. At first glance this looks like "machines that can think." It is not, but it certainly is a definitive change, a breakthrough.

How inanimate congregations of steel and wire and speeding electrons can do these things is the main object of demonstration of this book. That they do do it is no longer a dreamer's fancy. The machines and the men to improve them are here today. The breakthrough is out of the laboratory, in the "hardware" stage, ready to go to work. It only remains for the manufacturers of thousands of articles and services to learn what automation can do for them, and to give the designers and the scientists a chance to solve their particular production problems in the new way.

From the industrialist's point of view, the most obvious advantage of using machines that guide themselves is their enormous increase in uniformity of product and in speed. Once an automated machine is "instructed" to turn out an item of a given quality it will turn it out with essentially no variation. This has never been possible while human beings were in control. No matter how closely the standards are followed, human hands and senses are bound to vary in their execution of their tasks. Hence, a limit of error must be adopted in what the shop calls "tolerances." Such and such a shaft must be of the right diameter within one-half of a thousandth of an inch. This part and that part must fit together within a tolerance of one-tenth.

Elaborate and costly methods are needed to attain man-made uniformity in obedience to the chosen tolerances. Where the limits are extremely close, as they are in automobile engines and in the parts of fine instruments, complicated checking routines may be necessary, demanding highly expert and highly paid people. This "quality control" is the secret of modern production. It is the unique achievement of American mass manufacture that it can turn out a million parts so closely identical that they are interchangeable anywhere. Without this ability to make identical pieces, to fit with other pieces that may have been made thousands of miles away, mass production itself would be impossible. Quality control means cheap, plentiful goods.

The rigid checking-and-rejecting system at the root of it, however, is a critical link in the production chain. Standards are only as good as the specialists who determine them and the skilled people who measure the output against them. A good part of the headaches of any factory production chief stems from the constant battle to maintain acceptable tolerances all along the line, with human beings, no two of whom are alike, and no one of whom is like himself all the time.

Quality, nowadays, is often lowered in a compromise with speed. It is the first thing to be dropped when prices are slashed. We all know how frequently common articles fail to meet our expectations. Quality control has failed somewhere. Somebody let something through that didn't quite come up to specifications. Hardly anybody buys a car these days without finding a few things wrong with it. Small things, maybe, but irritating. The standard thousand-mile check-up on all new cars is an admission that the car must be "cleaned up" mechanically in the dealer's repair shop, to eliminate the odds and ends the factory has missed, as well as to inspect after the normal breaking-in period. Things that shouldn't be there are found: doors don't quite fit, the radiator drips, a bit of paint is off, the clock doesn't run. . . . Some human guardian of quality missed.

When you buy a pair of shoes you often find that one fits a trifle better than the other. You assume your feet aren't mates. They may not be, but shoe manufacturers admit freely that with the present system of man-operated shoe machines it is impossible to make a right and left shoe that are true mirror images of each other. It is a well-known practice to inspect each shoe as it comes off the factory line and mate it up with another shoe that looks like a twin. Thus the human eye and hand are relied upon to match pairs by individual experience. It's not a very accurate way.

Automation, as we shall see, is likely to improve shoemaking before long, just as it is already improving many other industrial arts. There is a middle ground of automatic production, a transition stage, which will probably come before thorough-going mechanization. It will catch up first with obviously backward parts of the industrial system. Truly mated shoes are in this class.

Or consider the mad addressing machine which in the early days betrayed *Time* and Miss Smith. These automatic printers will turn out thousands of postal labels in a short time, from a stack of address plates. Without them, mass mailings could never be managed. Such machines, however, have neither judgment nor a sense of duty. They are not interested in their mistakes or in what happens in consequence. All that part of it is up to the operator. Automation could easily fix it; no doubt plans are afoot for improved control of the machines.

A simple little addition called a "fail-safe device" would detect an error at the instant it was made and stop the machine. A small bump or indentation on each address plate, say, might act upon a lever and inform the machine that it had already printed that particular address. A repeat printing, because something had stuck, would be thrown out. Under such safeguards, Miss Smith could not even get two copies of *Time*.

If one added a few more "intelligence" elements, the addresser could not only discard its mistakes but would blink on a red light at the maintenance man's desk, calling for help. Meanwhile, it would bypass the faulty mechanism, if the trouble were not serious, and go on printing.

Some of the confusion as to just what automation is, comes from the fact that numerous self-monitoring features, mechanically as simple as this, have been in use for a long time. In a candy factory a complicated box-filling machine pours a steady stream of chocolates into cardboard containers which it makes on the spot out of long rolls of the material. To make certain that it gets the right number of candies into each box, the machine weighs it as it darts by on a conveying mechanism, and before it finally seals the box. If a chocolate has stuck somewhere, or if the supplying chute was a little too generous, the error in weight of just one candy is enough to alert the machine. Almost humanly, as you watch it, a metal arm moves out and flicks the offending box off the line, throws the carton away and returns the chocolates to the feed bin.

No one measures the liquid in milk or soft-drink bottles; automatic machines do it and have for years. Day in and day out, you never get less (or more) than you pay for. It would take half the population of a town to fill its bottles as uniformly as this, and as fast. Society couldn't afford any such waste of human time and judgment. Automation has long been the answer. It is an old story in the packaging of hundreds of products which can be made to flow through measuring devices. This is perhaps one reason why engineers are apt to be bored with people who cry out excitedly at this "Second Industrial Revolution." It has been here all along.

Automation, then, is the mechanization of judgment as applied to machines. It is, more broadly, a new way of thinking in the fields of commerce and industry. As we follow it through the next few years, we shall acquire a new respect for human brains and dignity; we shall think it absurd that men ever did, with heads and hands, the purely repetitive tasks that machines can do better; we shall use the greater capacities which we have to invent more and more of the "intelligent" robots and to compel them to spread over the earth a uniformly satisfying standard of living. In short, automation at its best is the enslavement of machines, that human slavery may be truly ended.

Perhaps the human touch will be lost a little in the transition. It will not be an important loss. Somebody once wrote a yarn about a girl in a shirt factory who tucked a note into the pocket of a particularly big shirt she was inspecting. The note eventually reached a lumberjack and he came after her and married her. That's the kind of thing we are going to give up with automation.

2 | WHY WE NEED AUTOMATION

It is not really economical to do things in a clumsy and wasteful fashion. It has taken the world ten thousand years to discover this. We in America think we have learned the lesson better than anybody else—for have we not the highest "standard of living" on the globe? Let us be honest. Is that standard really as high as it seems? Have we actually eliminated the wastefulness and clumsiness?

The answer, unfortunately, is No. In spite of our famous mass-production system, with its incredible speed and fertility, our use of *human* resources is still shockingly bad. Millions of people are doing only a fraction of what they are capable of doing. Modern mass-production techniques may be highly paid in dollars, but they are guilty of demands upon the human spirit as arrogant as the worst sweatshop of old. They set men to tasks that make a joke of their real skills and keep them there for life. They destroy their initiative and reduce their ability of self-expression to the language of machines that go *ga-dang, ga-dang, ga-dang* all day long. This subtle enslavement of the most advanced nation on earth to the greasy mentality of machines has written our standard of living almost entirely in terms of cars and TV's and self-defrosting refrigerators, thus making mental and physical captives of millions who could do better.

We have not rebelled, but have blithely built a society utterly dependent upon machines, but in which the machines are equally dependent upon society. The American people and its robots are locked in a grimy embrace, each one shouting for more. The human being, long dispossessed of his right to use his muscles, is also losing his right to use his head because, in occupying a little part of it, machines immobilize the rest.

The real capacity of the human mind is the capacity to love and to dream, to risk and to achieve, to struggle, to fail, and later to succeed. Machines don't ask these things of their human attendants, or often permit them. They are satisfied with the right touch at the righ moment and demand it forever. It is time that machines were deprived of their human slaves, for, as history has recorded so often, the slaves are better men than their masters.

Let's look at a case where the old and the new are in strong contrast. When I visited the famous Ford Engine Plant in Cleveland, I was deeply impressed by their success in forcing machines to take care of themselves. But I was more impressed by the gulf which lay between the men who commanded the automated equipment and those who were still pinned down to the old-fashioned routine, doing little things.

Side by side with the giant automatic broaches and boring mills is the assembly line, snaking here and there by overhead conveyor past hundreds of stations where men are making incredibly small contributions without even seeming to know it. As the engine blocks swing along on hooks suspended from the conveyor lines, locked into a procession that never stops till the day is done, each of these men dabs a little something on them. Here it is a bolt, there a sheaf of wires, again a carburetor, a breather pipe, a pump.

I stopped to watch the man who was fitting spark plugs into

their threaded holes. He didn't screw each one in tight but only started it. Somebody else finished the job later on. This fellow grinned and shrugged when he saw me, and shouted over the roar of the factory, "Anybody could learn to do this in twenty minutes."

While he told me about the havoc that would be caused if a plug were cross-threaded, and thereby magnified his own importance, a number of engines went by, giving him about a minute apiece to start six plugs. He didn't miss a single hole in the lot. A certain small complex of muscles in his hands—he used both—and a still smaller area in his brain were performing as an unerring team. He himself was talking to me, looking about the shop, listening to the clatter and the roar, chivvying in on the conversations of others. It was a kind of game with him—grabbing the plugs out of a box just so, giving each an expert twist, feeling the first thread catch, darting on to the next and the next.

He was cheerful, content, an expert, a master—at what? At doing a day in, day out job that any bush savage in Africa could do with a little training; a job no harder than his own child would meet in learning his letters by fitting wooden blocks into holes. A job, we hope, that automation can take away from him so that he can find work of his own size.

Amazingly, our high-geared economy is based on these tiny contributions which millions of people make, the majority of them with only a few per cent of their inborn skills. Is there any doubt that they are owed something better? Is there anyone who believes that we can *afford* to keep adult men and women at low-mentality tasks in the face of a soaring demand for more and more of everything? Surely we have taken the Industrial Revolution about as far as it can go in this direction. We are working toward a stalemate between men and the machines their grandfathers invented. More of the same will not break that stalemate. Only a change to machines that do their own menial tasks, on *their* own mental level, will break it. Automation.

As it is now, the human being can no longer supply his own wants with his own hands. A machine must do that for him, exacting as its wages that continuous small fraction of his capabilities but all of his working time. The real pressure for automation is the unconscious urge of the nation to extricate itself from a dangerous condition of human waste. It is true that in doing this menial task that the present machine demands, the operator earns enough money to permit him to buy the machine's products, and hence to maintain the level of the national economy. But is that a sound economy? It seems evident that in times of strongly rising demand and high prosperity, to entrust our future to a poor use of human faculties is to build on quicksand.

Economists, business authorities, engineers, scientists throughout the land are saying that productivity must increase enormously if we are to maintain our rate of progress. Productivity, they add, is not a matter of machines alone, but of machines and men. It is known that with present machines of the older style, the productivity curve is flattening off; there is not much more that can be gotten from the combination of big machines run by little brains. The only solution is to automate the machine, forcing it to take over the work of the little brain, and elevate the former human captive to the more skillful work of seeing that the machines are invented and kept running.

The rate of production increase is estimated by its most ardent apologists, the unions, at about 5 per cent per year. This, say the experts, is not enough. If some new way is not adopted to steepen the productivity curve, our standard of living will have to stop increasing also. It is this danger that lies uppermost in the minds of automation specialists. It is not a question of preventing automatic factories from engulfing us in wholesale unemployment. It is a question of re-educating the work

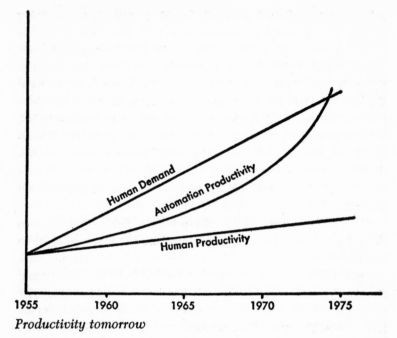

Productivity tomorrow

force fast enough to bring automation even at a slow rate. How, indeed, to induce management to look ahead and begin the shift soon enough.

I happened to be involved, many years ago, in one of the earliest cut-overs from manually-operated telephone exchanges to machine switching—the dial system. There were murmurs, I remember, that the automatic would put thousands of switchboard girls out of work. This was in 1923. The telephone company's answer seemed far fetched then. They said that if the girls continued to operate a growing system without mechanical help, by 1950 all the women in America would be working in telephone exchanges.

The communications industry was one of the very first to adopt automation in the broadest sense of the word, that is, as a long-range policy. The small, far-flung currents transmitting speech lent themselves naturally to the vacuum tube and other electronic gadgets. In fact, communication itself was largely responsible for the pioneering in this new art. It was a lucky thing indeed that the planners of 35 years ago realized the need for the automatic telephone. Without it, not one in a hundred of us could have satisfactory telephone service today.

We are confronted now with a rapid expansion of all consumer goods and services. Automation, which can extend production rates enormously and at the same time employ men's minds more fully, looks like the only valid answer. Human skill *must* be used to its utmost.

The Chinese coolie who works in his rice fields from dawn to dusk for a few pennies a day is actually far more efficient in the use of his resources than the fellow who screws in spark plugs at $100 a week. Measured at the level of his economy and standard of living, the Chinese is turning in a close-to-capacity performance. He may not measure up to our criterion, for he has no machinery and his methods are those of his ancestors. But he is not doing work that any child could do, nor is he enslaved to a machine. In his economy he is tied to the handles of a plow. In ours, we are equally tied to the handles of switches and levers. Which is the better man?

Many millions of Americans, it is true, are doing man-sized and dignified jobs: farmers, artisans in many trades, professional and business people. However, this is basically an industrial, not an agricultural society. It is industrial efficiency that counts.

There is yet another potent reason why we cannot afford to underemploy our national skills. This is the military exigency of the times. War cannot be fought today without machines— in fact, without highly automated machines. Under the emergency of the Second World War every shred of scientific knowledge was exploited by us and by our enemies. So startling was the advance in weapons, in aviation, and in automatic control that wholly new ground in every military field was opened up. It is unthinkable that we could fight another war, or even defend ourselves against attack, without the utmost use of all these discoveries and many more made since. Yet the whole thing would depend absolutely on our production ability in industry. The last time, it was possible to bribe the production forces with high wages and new privileges in order to turn out enough war materials. It won't be possible again because men are already close to their limit in their teamwork with present machines.

The scientific breakthrough has carried us beyond the limits of human endeavor, unaided by self-responsible machines. We cannot think or act fast enough to supply the control factors needed in modern production, either in peace or war. Only machines can "think" fast enough and accurately enough to operate on their new high plane of competence. Those are the machines we must have.

Suppose, for a moment, that automation lags and that our man-operated mass-production system continues to bear the brunt of demand. What happens if the demand begins to shoot up faster than it can stand? A sharp increase is universally predicted within the next ten years.

You may answer, simply build a few more factories and turn out more goods. But a "few more" will not be enough. Behind the production lines there is a vast network of vital supply lines: factories that make production machinery; mines and oil wells and forests that furnish raw materials; ships and planes, trucks and trains that move them; power plants that furnish their energy; colleges that supply their new technical and managerial blood; most important of all, thousands more of our citizens willing to work at all these jobs. Multiply the demand at one end of the line and instantly you multiply the entire network. A moderate increase in demand results in a far greater total increase, for it spreads out in the familiar geometric progression of the atomic bomb.

This is the same sort of self-multiplying expansion correctly anticipated by the telephone company long ago.

It is principally the threat of this runaway demand that has created so much interest in automatic factories. Because, so far as can be seen, if automation is adopted quickly enough it can meet almost any conceivable rise in production schedules. Provided, of course, that the quality and number of men for the new jobs is sufficient.

3 | HOW SOON?

This is something like asking, "How soon will I get rich?" How rich? How much automation is automation? The question is meaningless, because the rate of change in what constitutes automatic operation is so great that complete achievement tomorrow will undoubtedly be obsolete next week.

Many uneasy words have been written to prove that we are facing a second Industrial Revolution, but I can't find any responsible engineering or industrial leader who thinks that automation will "overtake" us in anything like the tidal-wave proportions often viewed with alarm by labor. Everybody else *but* labor is worrying that automation will come too slowly to deliver the goods that we shall need in the next decade or two.

Nevertheless, there was, in the last six or eight years, a very definite breakthrough in the science of electronics and communication, and this is what has given to automated machines the rather sudden "sophistication" which was lacking in even the most automatic of the conventional type. This is the revolution. So far, there is little reason to expect it to grow abruptly from a scientific to an economic one.

Ever since mechanization began we have been going through revolutions: TV brought one, the automobile brought one; the electric light, the telephone, the railroad, the steamship, the steam engine itself, all caused more or less violent upheavals in the ways of doing things and in the lives of the people concerned. But there is no record associated with any of them of permanent disaster overtaking anybody. So-called technological unemployment has followed them all to some extent, since at the start there are not enough people who understand how to run the new machines. But in every instance this unemployment has been quickly absorbed in two ways: by people quickly learning the new techniques, and by people obtaining jobs of the kind they were used to in the host of new industries that follow any great invention.

Nevertheless, when a new machine retires an old one, the workers directly affected are always confused. Seeing what they think is a mechanical behemoth overtaking them, they instinctively resist. It is this resistance, based on unsubstantiated fears, that is very difficult to evaluate in its effect upon automation. In the present, no one intends to throw great numbers of workers onto the street; no one would dare risk a major upheaval or breadlines or nationwide strikes, or sabotage. It is doubtful if the most sinister fictional ogre could do these things even if he wanted to. Automation is so expensive that it must come slowly; it is so complicated that it must demand the services of new thousands before the old ones lay down their tools. But the fears persist regardless of the paucity of the cause. It is possible that if those fears are enlarged enough, automation could be held back for years beyond the time when we ought to have it.

Probably millions of working people would be relieved to know that many thousands of businessmen, the "little" ones especially, are just as disturbed by this imaginary juggernaut. They know that automation means great change and they are reluctant to embrace it because of the many unknown quantities involved. Will they understand it? Will it save money? Will it do all that its advocates say it will? Will they throw money away by investing in expensive apparatus, only to find it obsolete before it is paid for? Is there not some way that they can put off the fateful decision?

For my part I would rather be a workingman in danger of losing his job than a businessman in danger of losing his business by making the wrong decision about automating his plant. There are always men in the business community with the vigor and the optimism to take the plunge. With keen imagination and the knack of putting their money on the right horse, they want to be in the vanguard of the new movement. A man like this will build a new plant that is automated to the limit, and steal away from the others a fat share of their markets.

Such is the case of Joe Hunter in California—a maker of venetian blinds. The trick in venetian-blind sales is to see how cheaply you can buy the material. Usually it is aluminum, rolled thin and given that slight hollow curve. Naturally, everybody can buy the stock from the large metal suppliers at about the same figure, in standard lengths. Production costs are then a matter of fabricating and assembling. Hunter decided that the way to beat the game was to learn to roll his own material out of aluminum ingots more cheaply, even, than the mill could furnish it.

So his company, the Hunter-Douglas Corporation, went to work on the problem and came up with a brand-new process, an automated casting and rolling mill combined. It required only one man to run it. The secret of the process, and of the lowered costs, was *continuous production:* raw aluminum ingot going in at one end and venetian-blind material coming out at the other all day, in one unending strip. Through automation Hunter had tackled, and in a limited way solved, one of the most stubborn problems in the metal-working industry—how to get away from the *batch* or piece process and make the material roll out of the mill like water out of a faucet. This is one of the greatest objectives of automation, for it speeds up production, permits the combining of many fabricating processes, and does away with costly handling charges.

In this case, Hunter not only seized a major share of the venetian-blind market of the whole country, but posted a challenge to the metal-working industry that continuous casting is possible for one aluminum product, so why not for others? And why not, indeed, for the steel industry also?

This determined pushing ahead by the imaginative pioneer in automatic processing is a factor that is bound to influence the automation time table. For what is to become of Hunter's competitors? For a short time, nothing. Then, as sales pressure develops upon them, they will have to fall in line and adopt the new production methods or go out of business. It is only a question of how aggressive the men like Hunter prove to be on the commercial front.

Put yourself in the frame of mind of the businessman who has a good product he has been making profitably for a long time. He would like to keep on at the old stand, with only "routine" improvement. He may own the business himself, or it may be a conservative family affair, interested in as little change as possible. You can appreciate how difficult the situation may be. Almost any day a Hunter may turn up and throw a monkey wrench into the nicely adjusted marketing machinery. What is our businessman to do? Ignore the challenge and depend on the tired old slogan, "Foremost in stoves (or brooms or toothpicks) for more than a hundred years"? Or must he plunge himself into automation and try to be a Hunter too?

It would be to the great advantage of the country if everybody were a Hunter, if industry as a whole were to move resolutely into the new ground, shoulder to shoulder, accepting the handwriting on the wall. If this should happen—it won't—there would be no closed factories, no displaced labor, no failing businesses. It would be like the war, with everybody so busy that nobody could possibly fall out of the race. Rapid expansion would more than care for job changes.

We are not made that way. Most of us are conservative, cautious, even timid. We make a religion of security; we like the smooth, gradual change and abhor sudden alterations in our way of life. With automation this pattern can be painful, even dangerous. The dislocations that will arise in these early days of change depend largely on the unevenness of our progress. Imagine an industrial town where automatic machinery sweeps in almost overnight. Here, management would be likely to dismantle old plants and erect new ones using half as many men, putting the other half "on the beach." Or, it might pull up stakes altogether and move to a location better suited to automatic factories. This would make our town into an economic desert. Meanwhile, other towns nearby might not be adopting automation at all, hence would be unable to absorb the displaced people.

This is what organized labor has a right to fear—an uneven mixture of the new and the old, with the comforting steadiness of employment gone and no one sure what will happen next. The drive for the Guaranteed Annual Wage contemplates a cushioning effect upon such chaotic conditions. All this will be a deterrent to the coming of automation.

Yet the most serious of all obstructions, the one most likely to cause extended delay, is the failing supply of young technical men. "When schools let out this spring," says a Westinghouse official, "50,000 jobs will greet less than half that many science graduates. And each year, despite the urgent need for trained engineers and scientists, the supply continues to go down. Technical personnel are in such demand that companies bid for their services in a manner often described as bordering on panic, stampede and chaos." The advertising pages of any newspaper will show you how true this is. On the threshold of the most inspiring and significant advance in technology in the history of the United States, there are not even enough technical graduates in prospect to supply industry as it is now.

If our education system does not manage to reverse this trend and pour out a rapidly widening stream of scientific people, automation could die in its cradle. It is the most advanced and difficult of the "disciplines" of applied science, demanding men of very broad training and high competence in many fields at once. Our youth at the moment does not seem to be picking up the challenge.

The focus of the trouble is not in the colleges but in the high schools. For some reason, much of our scientific spirit is withering just as it buds, in the teen-age group. This cannot be blamed upon the kids; no doubt they have as much talent for science as they ever had. It can be blamed, solidly, upon the parents and upon the teachers. Both seem unaware that a country which depends almost wholly upon technology must provide a generous supply of technicians to keep it going. This is a state of ignorance and complacence that may become suicidal unless education of the adults can get in its work before it is too late.

Contrast with this sad fact the situation in Russia today. According to Dorothy Thompson, every single school child is scrutinized for talent, and if and when it is discovered the State never again relinquishes its hold or permits the training to lag. The result of this, says the National Science Foundation in Washington, is that the Soviet Union, between 1928 and 1954 graduated about 682,000 professionals in the engineering field, while we turned out 480,000. One after another of our scientific leaders have taken to the platform to plead for more interest in science. Few have mentioned automation; all have been too much concerned with the technical starvation in the national defense. But defense is completely dependent upon automation now: what is bad for that is equally bad for internal progress too.

In somewhat lesser degree, automation is in danger of being

undernourished in its supply of non-college-trained technicians. The fact that the upgrading necessary will improve the wages and better employ human talents is not enough. How can all these men be trained, and how long will it take? It will take too long unless it is begun now, at once, before automation comes in. That this almost certainly won't be realized, either by labor or management, is a strong reason for a painful lag in automation. Its approach will be more of a seepage than a flood.

The history of all invention backs up this view. New devices and new methods are invented, and nothing much happens. Perhaps it is years before the steady, invisible pressure of rising demand forces them into use. Modern advertising does its share, but it works almost exclusively on the frivolous wants of humanity. It will be of little help to automatic factories. It takes many years for new ideas—big ideas—to filter through the whole body of the citizenry, and the adoption of any change or any fresh philosophy, however important it may be, is a slow, discouraging business. Only in wartime, when extreme urgency throws technical progress into super-high gear, do we get an effective use of what we know.

The one bright spot in the picture of oncoming automation is, in fact, the military one. Our military leadership has learned its lesson so well that now, in semi-peace, it is exploiting scientific discovery to the fullest extent, and providing the concentrated pressure needed to develop the new things fast. Automation is enormously the gainer by this, especially that fantastic branch of it which concerns the computers, or "mechanical brains." Just as war emergency developed the background for atoms for peace, so now the cold-war emergency may save the day for automation-for-peace.

The overwhelming consensus among informed people today is that automation is a tremendous advance in the effectiveness of living, but that it will come slowly—too slowly—with many a

false step and many a lag due to misunderstanding and igno-rance. This is a mature science, a sophisticated science. There are not nearly enough people who understand it or who can en-gineer and apply it. Its coming seems precarious and uncertain, and yet I believe that the American people will manage, as they always have before, when the stakes are great enough.

4 | AUTOMATION IS NOT NEW

Automation as a philosophy is new, a mighty breakthrough. But as a *tool* it is centuries old. In fact, it was an essential part of the Industrial Revolution, actually anticipating it by nearly one hundred years. Our venerable friend Aristotle is supposed to have remarked that it would help civilization if menial tasks were mechanized. All through the middle centuries there were men who sought to put this dictum into practice: Leonardo da Vinci, Galilei, Gutenberg, Leeuwenhoek, Newton— each with a contribution towards the emancipation of man by means of machinery. Most of these early attempts were meant to substitute only for men's muscles, so that more brute force could be exerted and more work done. Leonardo's airfoil and his piston pump, however, were more than this. They proposed to do something that man could not do. Likewise, with Galilei and his telescope and Leeuwenhoek and his magnifying glass. Through their successful efforts human senses were given new powers through machines. The printing press extended the written word into a new dimension, by automatically controlling the repetition of a printed page. It is hard to deny that these examples were, in a sense, automation.

There was little practical result from these inventions outside of learned circles. It was Thomas Newcomen's primitive

steam engine which opened the Industrial Revolution about
1725. From that point on, mechanization became a definite
goal that men thought of as affecting their lives.

Students of automation, however, generally give the Frenchman Denis Papin credit for the first intentionally contrived
device *to control a process automatically.* Papin simply put a
weight on the tightly fitting cover of a pot on the stove and produced the original pressure cooker. The invention soon broad-
ened to become a self-operating valve for relieving pressure at
some predetermined figure. It was ready to act as a safety
valve when the steam boiler appeared, and has been with us
ever since, probably the most common form of automatic control ever known. Today's pressure cooker is practically a duplicate of Papin's, with chromium plating. He made this important contribution in 1680, during the reign of Charles II.

During the eighteenth century the principle of self-control
of machines, crude as they were, went forward swiftly. There
were the windmills of the lowlands, enormous structures made
of oak, with sails fifty or more feet in diameter. The entire top
housing of the mill lumbered around on a circular track to
bring the sails into the wind, but was far too heavy for men
to "trim" by hand. Nobody knows who first devised the automatic steering mechanism for windmills; it was worthy of
modern times. It consisted simply of a miniature windmill
mounded on the turning head of the large one and facing at
right angles to the main sails. It was geared to the turning
mechanism and so could furnish the power to force the mill
into the wind. If the wind veered, it began to turn the small
sails and automatically adjust the mill back to the proper position. At the same time, the controlling sails *lost* the wind and
so exerted less turning effort. Back into alignment again, the
guide sails lost the wind altogether and did not work again
until the wind shifted once more. You had here, as Diebold
points out, a perfect example of what is now called "feedback."

Feedback is so important in automation that we will define it here. It is not complicated in principle, although extremely intricate in modern practice. The term simply describes an arrangement of sensing and powering devices which continuously detects the condition of an apparatus (or of a product made by an apparatus) and establishes the error between the actual condition and that desired. The error then produces a force which is *fed back* into the apparatus to correct the condition. When the error has been corrected, the feedback device ceases to operate. In more technical language this is called *negative* feedback, because the error is made to cancel itself out. Thus, the small windmill mounted on the big one always seeks to reduce the error in the heading of the big sails and is only out of operation when the sails are perfectly trimmed.

There are thousands of examples of feedback all around us. A common one is the cold control in your icebox. If the temperature inside warms up a little when you open the door, the thermostat turns on the motor and produces a little extra cold. The falling temperature influences the thermostat to turn off the motor again. Domestic thermostats and the one in your car's radiator circuit are true examples of feedback automation.

The human body is a marvel of feedback control, using it in many complicated ways. When you reach out your hand to touch something you use an intricate machine composed of eyes, brain, arm and hand muscles, and a network of nerves. You don't know it, but the system, as you make the reaching effort, constantly checks back with the optical center of the brain to learn whether the hand is approaching the chosen target. It is all done so rapidly and with such hairline control that you apparently go straight to your objective. The errors are there, however—thousands of them, canceling out, one after another at high speed, so that the *apparent* direction of the arm's travel is a straight line. A certain type of palsy called "intention tremor" is really a disease of the body's feedback system. The nerve control has become so sensitive that it over-shoots each time it corrects the error, and produces oscillations which appear as a constant shake. One of the toughest problems in electronic feedback control systems is to attain high sensitivity without running into this difficulty of oscillation.

But to go on with our historic view of automation: Early in the eighteenth century a young man named Humphrey Potter was put in charge of a primitive steam pumping engine invented by Newcomen. By grasping a handle, Potter admitted steam from the boiler into the engine cylinder so as to raise the piston. When it was raised he moved the handle again to cut off the steam and allow the piston to drop, thus pumping the water. Here was a good case of a man doing a job far too simple for him, and Potter realized it. Studying his two actions with the handle closely, he observed that the piston was always in a certain position when it was time to let in the steam, and at a certain other position when the steam was to be shut off. He reasoned correctly that the piston itself could be linked to the handle in such a way as to do its own turning on and off. When he tried it, it worked.

This was the forerunner of the slide-valve mechanism which has been used on every steam engine since, and in numerous other ways for the control of the flow of fluids in machines. A familiar example today is the valve mechanism in an auto engine. Here, a rotating camshaft lifts and drops the valves at exactly the right instant to admit gasoline vapor, and again precisely when necessary to open the exhaust line. There is no feedback here, although there is feedback in the engine's device for automatically advancing the spark. However, both examples are types of automation.

The world's first genuine automatic factory was built and successfully run over 170 years ago. This was the flour mill invented and used by Oliver Evans near Philadelphia in 1784. Evans had nothing but a stream of water to work with, yet by an ingenious use of waterwheel power and shafting he was able to handle his grain automatically, without a human hand touching the apparatus, all the way from kernel to finished flour.

Not only was Evans' mill provided with a kind of feedback that regulated the grinding process to give the right fineness to the flour; he also included three types of conveyor mechanisms for moving the grain from one pair of millstones to the next. This is essentially what the latest automatic automobile plants do, with mechanisms called "transfer tables." Thus Evans anticipated another essential feature of automation—the "automatic handling and positioning of parts between progressive production processes," as Ford defines it. Thus the so-called "Detroit automation" really began in Philadelphia.

Close on Evans' heels came the Scotsman James Watt with his great invention of the flyball governor for steam engines. The year was 1788. Watt had taken the old Newcomen engine, added a piston rod, crank, crankshaft and flywheel and had produced a continuously self-operating engine *that turned.* He had also added the slide-valve mechanism so that the engine fed itself properly with steam from an intake pipe. What he now needed was some way to control the flow of steam through the throttle valve so that every variation in power demand upon the engine would not alternately speed it up or slow it down— in other words, an automatic feedback sensitive to speed. In the crude mills of that day, with the engine turning many shafts through belts, any variation in power demand at one point would be reflected throughout the mill. To overcome this, a man had to stand by the throttle, continually adjusting it— again, a human being doing too easy a job for his brain capacity. Watt wanted to get rid of the man.

His answer was a small vertical shaft geared to the engine shaft and turned by it. On this shaft were pivoted two short metal arms with heavy metal balls mounted at their lower ends. As the shaft rotated, centrifugal force pulled the balls away from the shaft, where they spun around at some level dependent upon the speed of the engine. Metal links connecting the arms with a rod that turned the throttle valve on or off, completed the device. Thus, when the engine went too fast the balls would fly outward, raise the throttle rod, and close off the steam somewhat. The engine would then slow down, allowing the balls to sink a little and admit more steam. In practice the engine would "settle down" to a constant speed; if its load changed and its speed varied, the flyball governor would automatically adjust the steam requirements to restore the proper speed.

Watt's governor became as essential to a steam engine as its cylinder, because in virtually every factory loads varied while

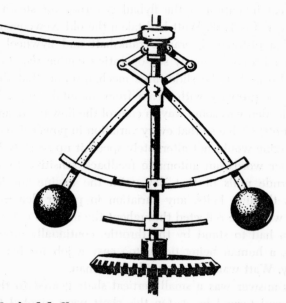

James Watt's flyball governor, an early example of feedback control

speed had to be kept constant. Actually, steam engines and turbines today are controlled by some form of flyball arrangement stemming directly from Watt. Nobody has thought of a better way to do it.

As the nineteenth century swung over the horizon, the marvelous age of applied mechanics moved in with an ever increasing rush. In the very first year—1801—while Jefferson was preparing his principles of American democracy, the Frenchman Jacquard invented an automatic loom which once more anticipated a fundamental principle of automation. In Paris that year, Joseph Marie Jacquard exhibited to the public a weaving machine that worked in obedience to steel cards punched with holes. Like the modern computing machine it could be "programmed" to produce an almost infinite variety of patterns.

The Jacquard loom met with instant success. By the year 1812 more than 11,000 were in use in France alone; the news that the century-old tradition of hand designing was now replaced by automatic means had begun to effect the textile industry in England and America. So intricate were the patterns that Jacquard could turn out that a world-wide fad started for weaving silk pictures of people and scenes. Every ruling monarch of Europe turned up in framed Jacquard pictures. Intricacies of pattern entirely beyond human hands became common items of commerce.

The world had now been given, over 150 years ago, all the basic elements of automation: automatic machines, feedback control, automatic transfer devices to move the product between manufacturing stages, a punch-card system which could "compute" each separate move machinery should make. The fact that automatic factories did not come in then, however, was not surprising. Except in a few special branches—textiles was one—there was no demand for speed or high production. The fundamental principles were known; it was now only a matter of demand. It should be evident that automation as a tool is not a discovery of the mid-twentieth century.

With the basic principles at hand and with the magnificent work in general science by Faraday, Maxwell, and a score more, automation simply waited until there was need for it. Need arose in several ways at the time of the Civil War. One of the most delicate and useful of applications was devised by Robert Whitehead to make his newly invented torpedo effective. He had been able to form the monster in the image of a fish and to drive it at high speed with steam engines of miniature size. But he had not conquered the tendency of the "fish" to "porpoise," to leap and plunge through the waves. This jumping made the torpedo's behavior erratic and its aim poor. What he needed was a control *sensitive to depth.*

Whitehead seized upon the aneroid barometer as the best means of detecting the depth at which a torpedo traveled. This was a device for continuously recording slight variations in pressure. He found a way to connect this "pressurestat" to the horizontal rudders of his craft and so maintain a steady level set before the torpedo was fired. This was an arrangement of feedback elements quite similar to the windmill control.

The invention had one bad fault. If it was made sensitive enough to maintain the torpedo's course at a given depth within a few feet, it fell into natural oscillation, causing the torpedo to weave up and down. The more sensitive he made it, the more exaggerated the weaving became, until the performance was worse than with no control at all. Sensitivity and power, it seemed, would not work together. Whitehead next tried a pendulum inside the torpedo, swung from the upper side of the skin. As the "fish" tried to porpoise, the pendulum moved forward or back and actuated the rudders to counteract the effect. This worked better than the barometer device, since the pendulum weight had considerable mass and tended to level out irregularities in the path of the missile. The first successful torpedoes were fitted with this type of control.

They were still pretty clumsy and traveled in a series of undulations which might, in rough water, ruin the aim at any moment. Here you had a first glimpse at feedback's worst enemy, the effect called "hunting." Since a mechanical control mechanism always has mass and friction, it is always a trifle *late* in compensating for an error. If it is sluggish enough it may be so late as actually to apply its correction in the wrong direction, thus increasing instead of decreasing the error. If it is less sluggish it may still be late enough so that the correction is carried too far, thus demanding a second correction in the opposite direction. This leads to oscillation. The control constantly "hunts" for the zero-error condition but never quite finds it.

You will find the same thing going on in the thermostat of your home furnace. A slight hunting action keeps the temperature of the rooms undulating up and down past the actual temperature you want. In modern form, as we shall see later, *electrical* controls have been given a damping factor which quickly kills this tendency to correct the error too enthusiastically. There is always some hunting, but it is not noticeable and never rises to the point of true oscillation.

The shock absorbers on the axles of your car are anti-hunting devices. When you go over a bump, the springs try to compensate for it by compressing without raising the car. They do not quite succeed. Alone, they would reproduce the bump a little later, and the car would behave as if it were riding on the back of a horse. The shock absorbers interfere with this and kill off the recoil of the springs before it can influence the car.

About the time that Whitehead invented his depth control, a steamship syndicate built the world's largest steam vessel, the *Great Eastern*. She was so big that no sailor was strong enough to turn her rudder by twisting the steering wheel. Hence, steam steering was necessary, an engine being installed at the stern to turn the rudder post through gearing. The steersman merely operated the engine throttle through suitable cable connections.

Many of the early steamships before the *Great Eastern* had used steam steering, but in her case it was soon proved that even with power to aid him a man could not keep the huge ship on its course. Hunting developed and the vessel zigzagged its way across the ocean. This was only one of the many troubles that beset this giant side-wheeler, but it was one that had to be cured. The cure contributed one more refinement to the art of automation.

What the designers added was a simple mechanical linkage between the rudder post and the engine throttle. As the rudder swung around in response to the engine's motion, it automatically closed down on the valve. This was called a "follow-up" linkage, and it acted to reduce the correcting effort as it neared the desired zero position, and in that way prevented overshooting, or hunting. Again, a clear case of negative feedback, but with a second negative added.

A few years later, in 1872, Joseph Farcot, in Paris, invented a slightly more advanced ship's steering engine. In writing of it he said, "We thought it necessary to give a new and characteristic name to this novel mechanism and have called it a 'servo,' or enslaved motor."

The servomotor or, more generally, the *servomechanism,* is today the heart of automatic control. Whether it is merely a bar of metal connecting two related parts of a machine, or a hydraulic engine, or an arrangement of electric motors, or even a complicated electronic circuit, its function is the one that Farcot envisioned. It permits very delicate impulses, generated by a sensing device, to be multiplied into power enough to steer a big ship or turn the switch that starts and stops your furnace.

Here, then, are the historic landmarks that anchor automation firmly to the Industrial Revolution. We see modern repetitions of them everywhere. Evans' flour mill is repeated in the giant plants of Ford, Chevrolet, and Chrysler—far different in speed and complexity, but basically the same idea of continuous flow of a product through a line of manufacturing steps. We see Whitehead's delicate torpedo control refined to a thousand times the sensitivity in the automatic pilot of the airplane. Whitehead did not have the hairline-sensitive gyroscope that Elmer Sperry devised during the First World War for his gyrocompass. But he realized the importance of having a reference point in space from which to guide military missiles. His pendulum was the first attempt to attain it.

We see the Dutch windmill-within-a-windmill of the seventeenth century repeated today in the tail-vanes of thousands of mills on our farms, and on every kite and airplane. We see the principles of Jacquard's loom spreading through tens of thousands of applications of the modern punch card. We use Watt's flyball governor every time we dial a number on the telephone.

Automation as a tool, if not as a philosophy, has been with us a long time.

5 | ELECTRONICS COMES OF AGE

The reason we have a mechanical age at all is that nature operates, so far as we know, in absolute obedience to her own unvarying laws. Every time a scientist, or anybody else, discovers another of these laws an opportunity is created for accomplishing practical results that could never be accomplished before. Automation seems new to us because until very recently we did not know the physical laws which would permit machines completely to take care of themselves. Their discovery is opening a new age.

I was just out of college and was working in a small research laboratory when a young man showed up with a discovery—perhaps a rediscovery—of one of these laws. This man, whose name was Spencer, was not a scientist but a furnace tender in a lumber camp. As he told his story, he had been put on night shift to keep the fire going under a donkey boiler that furnished steam for the saws. He had found it very troublesome to keep awake so as to tend the fire periodically, until he had noticed that the round metal door of the furnace snapped sharply as the fire died and it cooled off. Spencer made his bed near the boiler and was always awakened by the snapping door in time to replenish the fire. He noticed that the door snapped again as it heated up. He wondered now what made the door do that, and whether a piece of metal, slightly dished as the door had been might be put to some good use.

The head of our laboratory thought that it could. What Spencer had here was a thermostat, probably an original one in this special form of a dished metal disk. It looked promising because it was an "all-or-nothing" device. Thermostats then worked slowly and with annoying hesitation. The Chief saw a chance to make electric circuits critically sensitive to temperature.

This was a newly observed manifestation of the very well-known laws of thermal expansion. If one welded together two thin sheets of dissimilar metal such as steel and aluminum, and formed them into a very slightly bent disk and then heated the disk, the two components would expand at different rates, setting up stresses which, at some point, would be enough to turn the disk inside out. Cooling it again would restore it to its original shape. What the boss visualized, in that first half-hour of conversation with Spencer, was a disk fitted with electrical contacts that would be open when the disk was in one shape and closed when it was in the other.

Spencer went to work for us and two years later the thermostatic snap-switch was ready—a rather complicated little gadget a trifle bigger than a fifty-cent piece. The patents sold to a large electric manufacturer, reportedly for more than a million dollars. It has done duty ever since as the temperature-control

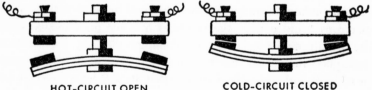

HOT-CIRCUIT OPEN   COLD-CIRCUIT CLOSED

Original Spencer thermostat

element in electric irons and coffee makers. It was a pioneer in
the field of domestic automation.

In the mid-nineteen-twenties, when the Spencer thermostat
came out, there was very little on the fire in the way of electrical control except for a few types of voltage regulator on
power lines. All attempts at control had been mechanical ones,
that is, "engines" of one kind or another. Their inherent weak-
ness was their sluggish action, resulting from their inertia.
While the thermostat was not electrical but electro-mechanical,
it no doubt suggested to our imaginative researchers that electric circuits could and should be used for control purposes.
These circuits had inertia, all right, but it was many thousands
of times smaller than mechanical inertia. Hence, electrical controls could be expected to work much faster. And along with
low inertia came practically instantaneous starting and stopping
of current.

Nothing in the way of electrical control was discovered at
that time, however, because the only way that a current could
be used to move anything or change anything was through a
motor or a relay. Both of these introduced mechanical components again, and these brought in the old difficulty of inertia.
A new principle was needed.

Early in the century Fleming and De Forest had discovered
that new principle in the vacuum tube, then called a "therm-
ionic valve." This remarkable little device worked by means of
a stream of electrons, so small and weightless that billions together were invisible. Nevertheless they could be used. By a
system of amplification within a vacuum tube, relatively few
electrons could control the destinies of huge numbers, so that
the infinitesimal power of an incoming radio signal could be
multiplied millions of times. The electron tube, of course, led
to radio broadcasting, but before that it had been applied to
the "repeater" stations on transcontinental telephone lines,
where its amplifying power ran into the billions.

Here lay the tools for instantaneous electronic control, but they were not recognized. Automation still had a long way to go on the mechanical side. During the years between the two wars, a great many advances were made in automatic machinery. Factories abandoned the use of single, large electric motors driving groups of machines, and came to employ large numbers of smaller ones, one for each particular motion or activity of a single machine. Various kinds of high-speed push-button switches were developed to give fast and flexible control. A great deal of work was done on electric motors to adapt them to the requirements of variable speed, fast starting and stopping, and light weight. There was no attempt yet to interlock the machines with each other or give them the power to monitor their own performance; that is, there was no automation.

Automation, however, was making headway elsewhere. In the chemical and oil-refining industries the need for electrical controls for processing fluids was paramount. Human hands could not move fast enough, nor could human beings risk the dangers inherent in many chemical processes. It was necessary to measure temperatures, pressures, rates of flow, and so on, accurately and continuously, and to adjust the complicated processes the instant anything went out of line. Hundreds of ingenious instruments were devised to show what was going on, and these were usually grouped in one room so that the operators could know every minute how things stood. Along with the indicating and recording instruments, most of them electrical, there were banks of remote-control switches and buttons which operated motor-driven valves all over the plant. In this grouping of control, these industries had taken the first step toward true automation. The next necessary step would be to join up the indicating circuits with the control circuits and make the plants self-operating. It required the pressure of a war to bridge this gap.

By 1940 radio broadcasting had settled down to a regular public service, receiving sets had passed the stage of experiment, roofs had lost their loads of crazy aerial wires and the new science of *electronics* was well begun. Television could be seen in the laboratory, pictures could be sent over wires or by radio waves, people could talk through the air from one continent to another. Then we were plunged into a new war so grim, so violent, so swift that only science could win it.

Emphasis for victory quickly settled upon the airplane. It was necessary to upgrade the art of flying to give greater range, speed, and firepower, and especially to make accurate shooting and bombing possible. Conversely, it was just as necessary, by countermeasures, to outwit an enemy who was doing the same thing. There was only one scientific tool capable of the job—electronics.

Dean Wooldridge, of the Ramo-Wooldridge Corporation, has traced what happened in a recent speech before a symposium on electronics and automatic control in San Francisco. He had been asked to answer the question, "How fast is automation coming?" and his answer was in the form of a historic example—the rise of electronics in the war.

As Wooldridge told it, the scientific attack upon the new military problems of the early forties began with radar—radar actually carried in airplanes for the purpose of locating an enemy and hitting him. Radar, to make the explanation complete, is a device for sending out short pulses of radio waves of very high frequency and receiving them back as echoes when the original waves hit an object in the air or on the ground. It enabled a pilot to tell in what direction and how distant the object was.

The first use of this amazing electronic system was as a simple aid to navigation. This was not enough, however. It was soon proposed that radar be used not only to *find* a target but automatically to aim the plane's guns or bombs at it. In other words, the scientists felt that an automated system was possible whereby the electronic machinery took care of the military side and the pilot merely flew the plane.

At the start this was only an imaginative dream, a "don't-you-wish-we-could" sort of thing. The problem was enormous: how to apply the lightning-fast action of electrons to tasks men's eyes and brains had always had to do. The military authorities tackled it by what Wooldridge calls the "black box" method, that is, by connecting a good workable radar in one package to a good workable gun-sighting system in another. The method didn't work. Somehow the black boxes disliked each other and got to playing games to see whether they could get in each other's way. In plain language, radar signals were not familiar to gunsight instruments which had always been used to human fingers. Mysterious mistakes in range and aim turned up and no amount of fixing seemed to correct them.

This situation did not last long, for the military soon saw its mistake. When the scientists pleaded for automation all the way, in a brand-new system, the Pentagon told them to go ahead. The proposition was to invent and design a single, integrated machine which received radar signals and delivered bullets or bombs. No black boxes tied together, but a new, highly "sophisticated" apparatus capable of only one thing, with built-in controls and automatic corrections. The problem was solved, in large degree, by the Radiation Laboratory at the Massachusetts Institute of Technology in Cambridge, Mass. The Laboratory, gathering in the finest brains available on our side of the war, became the birthplace of electronic automation.

The military urgency was so great that there was no time for the new art to be built, step by step, discovery by discovery, as it would surely have been done in peacetime. The idea for a new device might occur to someone on one day, be authorized that afternoon by telephone from Washington, be started in the design section next day, and actually be in operation in the air at the front within a month.

Not only the military specialists and the laboratory people, but everybody, pitched in. In thousands of small factories devoted to radio and TV, in dozens of large corporation research departments, in the laboratories of the telephone company and other communications organizations, teams of physicists, mechanical and electrical engineers, mathematicians, statisticians, professors—all threw their efforts into the common problem. The vast project mushroomed in temporary buildings hastily nailed together all over the country. The world's foremost scientific brains, leavened with brilliant young men who were still students, set out to build a new science around the behavior of electrons vibrating at billions of times a second. It was not a question of assembling knowledge already held, but of breaking virgin ground, making and recording basic discoveries, and applying them virtually at the same time.

The world has been taught that the atomic bomb was the one great scientific milestone of Allied war research. It is more likely that the future will grant to wartime electronics an equal share of credit in laying the groundwork for peacetime progress. Radar, the rise of mathematical computers through their use in gun-aiming instruments and in research itself, the proximity fuse, the guided missile, navigational aids such as Loran, plane-landing devices such as GCA, special detection systems such as IFF, which identifies "friend or foe"—all of these, and many others not publicized, were the products of the great drive to achieve electronic machines of war that did their own duties without human help.

It can fairly be said, I think, that most of this resulted from the determination of the hard core of scientists that the "black box" method of hooking together isolated pieces of apparatus must give way to a single, integrated system, engineered to accomplish one purpose. The upshot was the development of a new approach to all large technical problems—what has now come to be called "systems engineering." The customer, in this case the Pentagon, has learned to say, "We want to accomplish such and such an objective. We would like to do it in the air (or on the ground or under the sea). Please design for us an entire system, from the bottom up, that will produce the desired results."

War-born systems engineering used, among other things, a highly technical branch of mathematics now called "operations analysis." This involved teams of men from all branches of engineering and science, from business, economics, even psychology and medicine and the law. Depending on the nature of the problem, the project would begin with a broad general study of all possible factors concerned and gradually work down to the best attainable solution. Nothing was left to chance. The final product represented in every case the utmost in advance that human brains and mechanical brains together could achieve at that particular time.

This wholly new and dynamic approach to technology yielded an extraordinary advance, in particular, in electronics, for which the specialists have adopted the word "sophisticated." The advance centered around schemes of electronic control which summed up to a thoroughgoing method of automation: the principles on which automatic factories could be based.

The heart of the new knowledge was an understanding of electronic circuits and the behavior of streams of electrons vibrating at incredible frequencies. It was now possible to generate large blocks of electronic power in great tubes called "magnetrons" and "resnotrons," and to "pipe" this power through special cables and over air-borne beams for hundreds or thousands of miles. At the other extreme, it was possible to detect and amplify electronic signals of infinitesimal strength, using them accurately for triggering innumerable control processes. Further, great assemblies of vacuum tubes and their associated circuits could be made to *compute*, and to figure out in a matter of hours mathematical problems that would require years to do by hand. In addition, there were sensing instruments that would detect anything the human senses could detect, but do so with thousands of times the delicacy and accuracy and millions of times as fast.

In this way the stark necessity of war brought about a major scientific breakthrough into new ground that would be profoundly important for peace.

6 | HOW AUTOMATION WORKS

If a machine is to control itself it must supply the things that a human operator would supply. These fall into two classes: physical manipulation of controls, such as handles, wheels, buttons, switches; and judgment—the act of determining *when* to do these things. Modern machinery, which is generally called automatic, has already taken over practically all of the motions of cutting, grinding, drilling, boring, gripping, and positioning of the material which is being worked upon. It has not taken over the manipulation of controls or the judgment factor. So the problem of automation is mainly one of building judgment into a machine and tying it up with these physical controls. Until the advent of advanced electronics it was impossible to come anywhere near replacing human judgment with mechanical judgment. Now, because the behavior of electronic circuits has turned out to be remarkably similar to the behavior of certain human mental processes, it is possible to supply this missing link.

A problem of judgment can often be expressed in the old Aristotelian form of a syllogism: *if* this happens *then* that follows. This is a straightforward statement of cause and effect, and represents a situation which is continually present in everyday living. We make tens of thousands of cause-and-effect de-

47

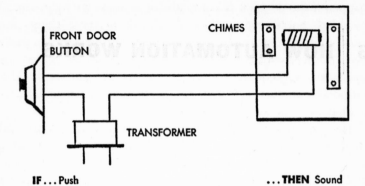

IF...Push   **...THEN** Sound

Simplest IF-THEN *automation, the familiar door-chime arrangement*

cisions every day; our bodies probably make millions of them in the same time. In fact, the brain is perpetually at work rendering small solutions to such problems. Now it happens that this cause-and-effect action can rather neatly be translated into mechanical and electrical terms. Basically, we have only to work out a sensing element to detect when the *if* condition is present, and connect it in a workable way with some *then* device which will merely carry out the duty when the *if* device gives the word.

A common alarm clock is an *if-then* device. Its owner determines the *if* factor by setting the small hand at the figure 7 on the dial. This positions a small disk with a notch in it. The *then* mechanism travels around with the hours and when it arrives at the notch it drops a lever into it, which in turn releases the catch on the bell clapper, and the bell goes off. There are countless such arrangements in the world around us.

When the human brain makes a decision, it is apt to surround the *if* condition with a great deal of complication. Considerations such as preference, a knowledge of consequences, a desire for a specific result, and a general awareness of what may happen if the decision is not made, or is made wrongly, are all included. Surprisingly, all or nearly all of these things are closely tied to *past experience*. It is doubtful whether we make even the most intricate decisions without drawing generously upon our store of experience in similar circumstances. This introduces another act, and it is a fundamental one in automation, too: the act of *comparison*.

The human brain contains a vast library of neatly ordered single facts. An important element in the process of learning is the act of receiving through the senses some new fact and of cataloguing it and filing it deep within the brain. From that moment forward, the use of that fact involves an act of *memory*.

In its search of memory for the material to be used in decision-making, the brain works almost as fast as an electronic device; in fact, it is now considered possible that it may be some form of electro-chemical process. Not only a single item of stored fact, but thousands, may be looked up and assembled to make even a simple decision. The mechanics of the job are carried on below the conscious level; we are aware only of the summation of it all.

Using this general definition of decision-making as a guide, it is not too difficult to put together a system of electrical and mechanical elements that will do the same job, in an elementary way—that is, the job of making and carrying out a decision on the basis of certain "remembered" facts. It is only necessary to find a way to store these facts in such a form that a mechanical device can appreciate them and act on them.

The first requirement is a uniform *code* in which all desired facts can be stored; the second requirement is a *sensing* element that will continually appraise a controlling condition; the third is a *comparing mechanism* that can measure the remembered facts against the sensed condition. And the fourth is a *triggering device* which will automatically operate when the comparison of facts and condition becomes an identity. Between them, the fact-storage member and the sensing member establish the *if* part of the equation, while the trigger and whatever apparatus it is that carries out the orders, constitute the *then* portion of it.

In automation applications it is desired to cause a machine to monitor the results of its work. For that purpose a standard is set up in the "brain" part of the apparatus. It may be a standard of length, of size, of weight, of volume, of color, or of speed, pressure, or temperature. In any case the standard appears as a code. The code may be a simple position of a lever, or it may be a complicated pattern of holes in a punched paper tape. The coded standard represents the stored facts in the "memory," comparable to those stored in the human brain.

The machine also contains a sensing element, a detector which can appreciate the condition of the product being made, which it is desired to control. Again, this will be a length, temperature, and so on. This sensing element is so arranged as to translate the results of its observations into the same code as that understood by the memory. Now a comparing mechanism comes into the picture. The coded standard and the coded observation come together in it and are compared. When identity is established, an act is performed by the machine to deliver the product to another machine.

This is the most elementary kind of automation, without feedback. It is useful mainly in such simple operations as filling containers to just the right level. It is essentially a *measuring* operation. It follows the *if-then* pattern and may add an *if not-then not* faculty also. But it represents the beginning of judgment in machines.

A familiar example of such a machine is an ordinary door lock. This device is capable of only two things: it holds the door in a locked condition or it holds it in an unlocked one. It changes from one to the other when a specially coded order is presented to it for comparison with its "memory." In this

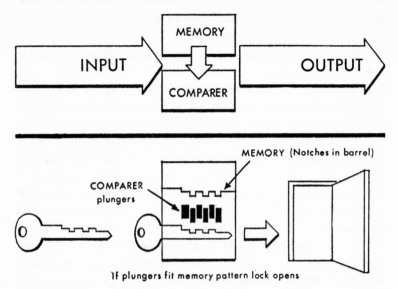

Basic open-loop automation system showing analogy in a common door lock

case of automation the triggering effort and the power to operate the mechanism remain with the human hand. But it is automation all the same.

When you insert your key in the lock, you present the mechanism with a new condition in coded form—the teeth on the key. A series of plungers is moved within, to conform to this code. The lock is now comparing this outside condition with coded facts stored in its memory. These facts are represented by a series of notches cut in a bar. If you have the right key, notches and plungers correspond. When you turn it the lock works. You are in.

The mechanism is merely a slave, though automated, and a complete moron. You can't unlock the door by talking to it, by tapping it, or by sending it a letter. The mechanism understands only one code, that of the notches on the key. It can distinguish between right and wrong in that code, nothing more. This is judgment, but only of a very limited kind. Yet within its limits nothing better than a lock has been devised. Try the wrong key. The lock detects it instantly and refuses to act.

One might add an interesting sidelight here. A lock-picker comes on the scene. He has certain tools that may fool the lock. Although it can distinguish between right and wrong, the lock cannot always tell the *shades* of right and wrong. One of the problems of automation in more complicated forms is that of devising a code of operation which can't be "broken" illegitimately by supplying a condition that is bogus but nearly identical with the right one. Banks have spent much money on this and have solved it by setting up a combination of conditions, all of which must be fulfilled before the lock is satisfied. If the lock misinterprets one condition, it will be pretty sure to correct its mistake on the next.

This is an over-simplified example of automation. A more "sophisticated" form of it involves a factor you might call "responsibility." That is, a sense of conscience about its mistakes. This is where feedback comes in. We have the same elements basically: the memory, the sensory organ, the comparing device, and the triggering mechanism. Then we add to those a mechanism that measures the outside condition against the standard condition *all the time,* and produces, in code, a force that is a measure of the error between the two. If the machine is working well, the error is usually very small and the force represented by it must be amplified before it can be used. After this is done, the error force is sent back to that part of the machine which is doing the work—cutting, grinding, and so forth—and is combined with the motive force of the process to alter that process. This alteration is so applied as to correct the error.

Since the feedback system is at work continuously measuring the error, it will know when the error is corrected, and will

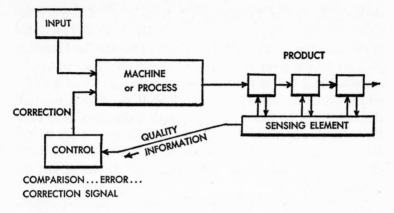

Feedback or closed-loop automation

cease to function when there is no error. However, it will go back to its work the instant a new error appears and perform the same routine again. In practice, the error is not a mistake, but an excess or a deficit in the activity of the machine which is under control—a deviation from ideal performance. Such a feedback system is like a father pushing a child in a swing. He does not push much with each back-and-forth motion, but just enough to keep the child moving through the same path. He is compensating for the "error" which gravity and wind resistance are constantly trying to introduce into the swinging pattern.

Again, looking at an actual example of feedback automation, suppose you want to receive through an automated pipeline a certain number of gallons of fluid per minute. The automatic control consists of a valve to regulate the flow and a meter for measuring how many gallons per minute come out. The meter is the sensing element, the *if* detector. Its readings are flashed by electricity or some other swiftly acting medium to a central control point. Here the readings are continuously compared with a fixed, steady reading you have set up to represent the desired rate of flow in the pipe. If there is any difference between these two it appears as an error. This error will be coded in the same way as the meter reading and the standard reading, perhaps in the form of an electrical voltage. This voltage is amplified and fed in the form of a power current to a motor which works the valve in the pipeline. If the flow is too fast, the motor will be made to turn in such a direction as to close the valve down; if too slow, the motor will open it up. As the flow approaches the desired amount, the meter finds a dwindling error and brings the motor to a gradual halt at just the right moment.

Now, it is quite possible for the system to be handled without automation. A man can stand by the valve, watching the meter and turning the valve wheel up or down as his judgment directs. This is what you do when you steer a car, adjusting with very slight motions the small error that results in "weaving." For driving an automobile it is all right, but for handling a mechanized process where the forces to be controlled are enormous, a man is not so good. He neither has the strength nor is his power of decision quick enough to maintain smooth operation.

The case of continuous papermaking will demonstrate the point. Here, a sheet of wet pulp is whizzed along on a wide belt, passed through groups of rollers to squeeze it to the right thickness, then carried still further to dry. The speed may be fifty miles an hour or more. Before automation invaded the field, it was necessary to stop these great machines frequently so that workmen could measure the thickness of the sheet with micrometers. If they found any part that was thinner or thicker than the required standard, it had to be cut out, the machine readjusted and started up again. In a few moments it had to be stopped once more to check results and see if the readjustment had been correct. If it was, the mill could go on making paper till it was time for another test by hand.

See what happens today in an automated mill. At the point where the paper emerges from the rollers there is a small piece of some radioactive material, radio-strontium, for instance. It gives off steady rays which penetrate the paper but are weakened in proportion to the thickness of the paper. On the farther side of the paper there is a radiation detector, capable of measuring very accurately the strength of the rays. The detector thus "knows" at every instant what the paper thickness is. It can easily measure down to a few ten-thousandths of an inch.

As the paper rushes along, a record of its thickness is continuously transmitted by the ray detector (by means of an electrical voltage) to a comparing device on the control panel. Here it meets up with a standard voltage representing the thickness of paper desired. An error voltage is thus generated, by comparison. This is amplified to sizable proportions by vacuum tubes, and the "built-up" voltage is introduced into a servomechanism which is powerful enough to control an electric motor connected to the paper-mill rollers. The motor can run either way, raising or lowering the rollers by very small amounts

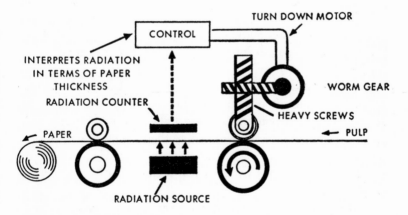

High-speed continuous paper thickness gauge

and hence controlling the paper thickness. If the rollers go up or down too far during adjustment, the control system brings them back instantly and the paper, held to a rigid standard by automation, can be rolled out with no stops at all.

One might ask, parenthetically, what becomes of the men who used to use micrometers on the paper, stopping and starting the mill. The new mill has many new jobs for them. The control system is complicated and requires continual supervision and servicing. With the new very high speeds and non-stop operation, the machine requires extremely alert human judgment all the time. There is less menial labor required, but more responsibility, and hence more skill and over-all knowledge of papermaking. If some men are no longer needed, there are sure to be jobs available in making the gauges and control systems that never existed before.

These two examples give an elementary idea of what it means to automate a machine or process formerly done by human skills. It is obvious that the skills were not very great and could well be dispensed with in the interest of improving human employment.

Automatic-control designers have little difficulty in finding effective means of observing and measuring conditions—the first link in the automation chain. If it is a position of something, a feeler like a lever or cam will do; if it is a color or the level of a liquid in a vat, a beam of light may be employed. If it is the thickness of a swiftly moving sheet of paper, plastic, or metal, radioisotopes and Geiger counters will serve. Or X-rays. They can penetrate where light cannot. If it is a temperature, a great variety of recording thermometers and thermocouples stand ready. Any of these can be "coded" so as to transmit their observations by electrical means to a central control point.

Putting the error to work, however, poses a more difficult problem. Since it is rarely more than a few per cent of the magnitude of the forces it monitors, it is too weak to be used directly to control them. The difficulty is further magnified by the requirement that the error force must remain in control as it declines toward the vanishing point. It is therefore necessary to introduce huge magnifications without altering the character of the error. To be useful, the resulting forces must be large enough to run powerful machinery. In effect, a team of horses must be controlled by the weight of a postage stamp. In a steel mill rolling operation, for instance, requiring driving motors of some 10,000 horsepower, an infinitesimal variation in the tension of the thin steel sheet is enough to hold complete control over the motors. Anything really wrong will bring them to a dead stop in four seconds. We will see later what an enormous multiplication of the tiny forces caused by the variation is needed to do this.

There are various ways to build up the flea power of a sensing instrument into brute force. One is to amplify the tiny signal with vacuum tubes to the point where the current can operate a solenoid switch controlling a heavy motor. Another is to cascade motors and generators in many steps from pigmy to giant, each supplying the team next beyond it with control current. Still another method uses hydraulic pressure to operate the control valves of a hydraulic motor. In the automatic transmission of your car a flyball governor arrangement is used to close such valves as the speed of the car increases, thereby shifting automatically from low to high.

A far more delicate application of this principle was found highly successful in the late war. Experience showed that the gunner in a tank could not keep his aim while pitching up and down over rough ground. Clinton R. Hanna of the Westinghouse Research Laboratories solved the problem by installing a tiny, fast-spinning gyro in the tank. No matter how the machine bucked, the gyro remained level. Electric contacts on it

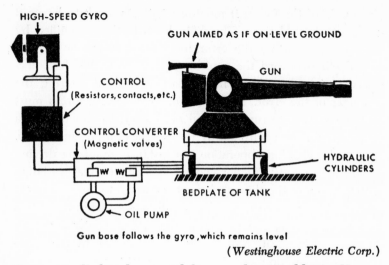

Gun base follows the gyro, which remains level

(*Westinghouse Electric Corp.*)

Gyro-controlled tank gun stabilizer used in World War II

operated a magnetic valve in an oil-pressure line which fed a large hydraulic cylinder that moved the gun mount. The effect of this was to keep gyro and gun mount locked together, and firing became accurate over the worst terrain. Eighty million dollars' worth of this simple automation was supplied to the Allied armies.

The fourth and probably the most versatile form of translating error-power into control-power combines high electronic amplification with a special type of alternating-current motor called the *selsyn*. It is possible to build a motor in such a way that when it is connected by three wires to a second, nearly identical machine, the two will lock into step and turn at identical speeds as accurately as if they were connected by solid shafting. They behave like identical twins, starting, stopping, and varying their speeds in unison. If the shaft of one is turned slightly, the shaft of the other follows, in either direction. The wires may be miles long and it is even possible to connect the two by radio. If you mounted a pointer on one and set it to some reading, say, on a clock face, the pointer on the other would give the same reading.

These gifted little devices were first used as "repeaters" for just such things as dial readings. A master gyrocompass on a ship was mounted far below decks where it could be well protected. To its card was fixed the rotating element of a small selsyn machine. Repeater compass cards, driven by selsyns, could then be installed all over the ship and would all read correctly, with no other connection than the three small wires running back to the master.

As it applies to automation, the selsyn system is used both to transmit error information and to magnify its small power into the large "torque" required to adjust a mechanical process.

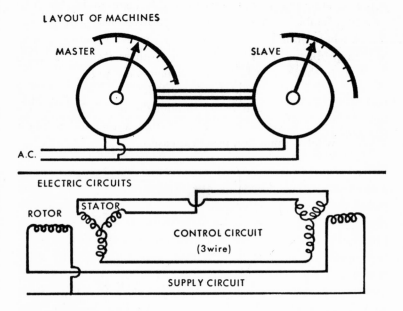

Elementary selsyn system

The combination of electronic amplification and selsyn motors will take care of nearly all problems of control.

We have now had a preliminary look at the main elements of an automated system: a method of measuring the results of a machine's work; a device for comparing this performance with a pre-set standard, thus computing the error; a transmitting and magnifying system for bringing the enlarged error to bear upon the controlling mechanism of the process.

The details of this system are extremely complicated because it works at such extreme sensitivity that it easily becomes prey to errors of its own. The feedback or closed-loop system of control can, for example, fall behind in its work enough to cause hunting, and if allowed to build up this effect, will fall into oscillation and may "run away." Its sensitivity is limited by many factors which have to do with the behavior of electronic circuits, and highly ingenious measures have to be taken to secure a "stable" system that is also positive enough to be useful. A whole branch of mathematics has grown up around these design problems. Every control job requires its own detailed analysis in theory first before the elements are put together. As there are several books and many articles in print which deal with control theory, it is better to omit the details here. It will be of more interest to look at an actual automated machine and see what is done in a practical case.

7 | THE ENSLAVED MILLING MACHINE

A few years ago a manufacturer of propellers for helicopters approached the Massachusetts Institute of Technology with the idea that perhaps a machine could be built that would turn out these items automatically. A propeller has an intricate and irregular shape; it is a highly skilled job for a fine machinist to set and reset his machine to take the many cuts from the blank that will yield the beautifully streamlined curves of the propeller. A large part of his time is spent in removing the blank and resetting it between cuts. Extreme accuracy is required from start to finish.

The manufacturer's suggestion was that a standard milling machine, which cuts metal in straight lines as a plane cuts wood, should be fitted with an automated control that would obey the commands of a master record printed on tape, making all the necessary cuts without removing the work from the machine, and without the use of a skilled operator.

Both the M.I.T. Servomechanisms Laboratory and the U.S. Air Force took an immediate interest in the problem, and under Air Force auspices the Laboratory agreed to make a general study of it. This they did, with paper results that were so encouraging that it was decided to build an experimental unit. No propellers were ever made because when the machine was

61

finished it was found to be so versatile and so generally useful that a number of commercial machine builders undertook to develop it further for wide application to machine-shop work. There are many such machines today; in speed and accuracy they can outdo the best machinist. And they can do, with standard equipment, many jobs that no machinist could do at all.

The machine chosen for the experiment was a large standard model, big enough to pretty well fill a two-car garage. Though extremely massive and complicated in design, the milling machine is quite simple in principle. Work on the metal being milled is done by a rotating cutter with blades on sides and bottom, which is supported vertically by a massive headframe. Below this the workpiece travels back and forth or to right and left, clamped securely to a heavy bedplate which runs on rails and is driven slowly by the turning of a threaded bar or lead screw. The cutting head can be raised or lowered to remove metal at different levels. The workpiece itself may not be very large. The great bulk of the machine is necessary to maintain high precision. Each motion of the bedplate and the rotation of the cutter is provided by an individual electric or hydraulic motor, with its separate control.

When operated by a human attendant, only one straight cut is made at a time. If a diagonal cut is wanted, the workpiece is clamped so that one of the two horizontal motions of the bedplate is used. If cavities in the top of the work are to be milled out, the piece is held stationary and the cutter is lowered to do the job. Sometimes, by operating handwheels attached to the lead screws, a good machinist can produce a combined motion of cutter and work so as to mill out simple curves, but this is a highly skilled operation.

Considering its size and cost, a large milling machine, in the hands of even the best operator, has very limited talents. It is used mainly to plane off flat surfaces such as the undersides of the legs of electric motors and the bases of castings. Nevertheless, a large amount of work is always waiting for it. The machine is one of the commonest in every large shop. Most shop owners would be delighted to have the machine more versatile than it is—for instance, to have it shape and finish curved surfaces or make irregular cuts. The team of man and machine cannot do these things; the man would have to have three or four hands and be able to keep his attention in several places at once.

When the M.I.T. engineers tackled the problem they began by considering the three types of motion the machine can perform: back and forth, across and back, up and down. They knew that by suitably combining the three, and by varying each one progressively, it would be possible to form almost any kind of rounded surface on a piece of metal. To automate the machine successfully these three motions would have to be controlled by some sort of prepared code containing "orders" for the instant-by-instant behavior of the three elements.

If you move a pointed stick through the sand with a simple right-and-left motion, you will draw a straight line. But if, at the same time, you rotate your shoulder a little, the combination of the two motions will produce a curve. Muscular coordination is so beautifully controlled in the brain that we can draw all kinds of curves without a thought. Writing is nothing more than this. Yet to invent a machine that could write is one of the toughest problems in engineering. It hasn't yet been solved.

What you do when you write is to move your hand vertically and horizontally across the paper with a rapidly varying proportion of each motion. Training children to write is simply a process of teaching the brain to manage these varying proportions of motion according to an intelligible pattern. The Laboratory's efforts were directed toward "teaching" their milling machine how to "write," on a piece of metal, in a very similar way.

For the sake of simplicity in describing their achievement, we will consider mainly the two horizontal motions of the machine, remembering that in actual fact the third motion—of the cutter up and down—was also included. Since the forming of a true curve by combining two motions of the bedplate would have required continuously varying speeds of these two motions, the inventors themselves adopted a simplification, or approximation. They decided to consider a curve as a series of very short straight lines joined together. By making each one about 1/100th of an inch long, virtually a smooth curve would be produced. Thus, during the cutting of one of these "differentials" of travel, each of the motions of the bedplate would be made at a constant speed, and the orders controlling the activity during that short interval would remain unchanged.

In practical terms this meant that, during any one 1/100th-inch interval, one driving motor would be turning its lead screw at such a speed, while the other would be turning at a different speed; both, however, would be steady. Meanwhile the cutter, revolving in a fixed position, would shave a flat surface along the workpiece, its direction being diagonal to the front of the machine.

This operation was to continue only for a very short time— not more than a few thousandths of a second. At the completion of it, one or both motors would change speed in such a way that their new combination would produce a surface in a slightly different direction. By doing this progressively across the workpiece, whatever curve had been "programmed" into the machine would appear on the work.

The problem had now resolved itself into a large number of simultaneous instructions to the two motors, a kind of working schedule or pattern, in a language that a motor can understand. Since the motors in this case were hydraulic rather than electric, their language was simply a rate of flow of oil through them. In other words, the speed of each would be determined by the exact position of the valve admitting oil to it.

We can now see how simple this part of the problem really was. The cutting of any single element along the surface of the workpiece could be ordered in terms of a particular setting of the two motor valves.

The next part of the problem was considerably more difficult. How were they to bring the valves to new settings after each 100th of an inch of travel? Here we come face to face with the most sophisticated of all the elements in automation: the computer. Basically an adding machine, the computer is composed of groups of electronic switches, relays, and storage "memory," which can be programmed in advance to carry out certain mathematical processes and issue the results in the form of coded instructions or records. This "output" can be in the form of numerals printed on paper or flashed on a screen, or a track on a magnetic tape, or it can be stored temporarily in coded form in a bank of electrical relays. The instructions or programming entering the computer can also be in many forms, one of the simplest being a pattern of holes punched in sequence on paper tape about an inch wide.

The Servomechanisms Laboratory chose the punched paper tape for input instructions and the bank of relays for containing the computed orders to the machine.

Delaying for the moment an explanation of how the paper tape is provided with its pattern of holes, let us follow it through the computer and see how the pattern is translated into actual machine motions. The tape holes are arranged in groups, each group consisting of several vertical rows side by side. There being room for seven holes across the width of the tape, there are a good many possible patterns of holes and no holes. Each vertical pattern represents a "bit" of information, and the combined significance of a single group of these vertical patterns is one complete instruction to the two motors on the machine. As it goes into the computer, the paper tape proceeds steadily for the length of one such group through a "reader," transmitting its information into the computer. The reader consists of a series of small metal fingers rubbing on the tape, in such positions that when a hole in the tape passes beneath a feeler it permits an electrical contact with a metal drum beneath the tape. The resulting closure of that particular circuit operates a relay inside the computer and that fragment of information is thus apprehended or learned. One can get an idea of this operation by comparing it with one of those small music boxes in which a drum passes beneath a bank of tuned metal reeds. As the small protruberances on the drum contact the reeds, a pattern of sound is produced and music results.

Now let us imagine that the tape has been read to the extent of one group of coded holes. The results are now stored in the relay bank as actual on-or-off-positions of the various relays. It has only taken a second or so to do this. Actually, the tape is somewhat ahead of the operation of the machine, storing the signals in advance. *Two* banks of relays are working, one instructing the machine while the other is clearing an old instruction and absorbing a new one.

The route of the instructions for any one motion, from relays to machine motors, is through a rather involved coding apparatus which translates the on-or-off conditions of the relays into pulses. These pulses are in the form of little "beeps" of alternating electric current which are fed to a servomotor or member of a team of selsyns. A feedback circuit is included here to maintain a continuous check. The actual *position* of the shaft of the servomotor thus becomes an indication of the position of the valve on one of the hydraulic driving motors on the machine *and also* of the shaft of a second servomotor, connected to the machine to check back with the computer. This is a second example of feedback. It is necessary because the computer must know whether or not its orders have been precisely carried out. It can also tell when the order is completed and thus when it is time to send along the next order. Without these feedback checks, the machine would be little better than one operated by human hands.

Tracing back now to the paper tape, how were the holes arranged in their peculiar patterns intelligible to the computer and the machine? Here is the most complicated part of all, and the part that lifts automation out of the "hardware" class into the hands of the graduate engineer. Coding the holes in the tape is another name for programming the computer.

All shop work in metal begins with a drawing or blueprint showing all dimensions of the desired product, all surfaces, curved or straight, all holes, together with information about the tolerances allowed. The prints are covered with figures calling for dimensions in inches and fractions of inches. When a machinist turns out an item by hand on a milling machine, he first studies the prints and plans out the schedule of operations to be followed—the cuts he must make in order to arrive at the final shape. Then he clamps the rough metal piece, usually a casting, onto the bedplate of the machine and begins his first cut. At M.I.T. the same planning steps are followed, but instead of interpreting the prints in terms of actual positions of the workpiece and lengths of cut, a schedule is written up to cover the whole operation in one continuous cut from start to finish.

This work is done by a couple of trained engineers who understand both the rules of shop practice and the language that a computer is familiar with. These engineers are fond of calling a computer an "idiot," because it does not have the imagination of the machinist and has to be told exactly what to do at every instant. If any instruction is missing or incomplete, the computer will give up and quit. A man will bridge a gap like that by using his own judgment and experience. The computer, having neither, and finding itself on unfamiliar ground, will do nothing but wait.

Thus, in writing up the instructions which are to appear on the punched paper tape, no mistakes can be made, and the whole pattern must be conceived in perfectly logical order. In the early days of the experiment with the milling machine, one of the relays in the computer began to weaken and occasionally to fail. This represented a false bit of information. Receiving it, the computer would go haywire and scramble the work. It took a month of intensive research to locate the trouble and replace the relay.

Interpretations of the original prints of the product are written down somewhat in the way one would plan a route for a vacation trip. You start here, go along this highway to that place, then turn and take another highway to another place, and so on through to your starting point. What the engineers have to do is to devise a route—the actual route which the cutting tool is to follow through the metal piece—which will be the most economical and at the same time follow a logical sequence. It has some aspects of solving a maze puzzle, in which all dead ends must be avoided and a path laid out which does not repeat anything. There are thousands of possible paths, but only a few which are suitable. So it takes many hours of study and planning to chart the best course, and an intimate knowledge of the computer and what it can understand, to avoid straining its intelligence too far. Usually, the programming job for a simple piece of milling work takes two men about two days' time. This is work a shop mechanic cannot do today, but it is quite probable that he could be trained to do it.

When the schedule has been made out, it will be in the form of a column of figures, or co-ordinates, expressing the motions of the milling cutter, broken down into a large number of short straight lines. Something like the sailing directions for a ship— so far on a course of 119 degrees, so far at 157, and so on to destination. This schedule is then typed up by hand on a tape-coding machine. As each figure is typed, punches inside perforate the paper with one vertical row of holes. The cut tape, when finished, is "read back" through another machine connected to the first and reprints the original list of numbers. A careful check then shows up any errors. The correct tape is then reeled and loaded into the reader of the computer.

Out in the shop, when the work is ready to start, the blank piece of metal to be cut is positioned carefully on the bedplate of the machine by a shop workman. He need not be a skilled machinist, for all he needs to know is how to set the work up according to simple instructions and tighten the clamps. In a pinch, even the Ph.D.'s who program the job can do it.

Described in this brief way the automatic milling machine may seem confusing. Admittedly, the electronic details have been left out. Certainly it was not an easy task to apply well-known computer theory to a specific problem. Which is all the more credit to the M.I.T. men who worked along on paper for several years before the machine itself was put in operation. As you see it today, the installation is remarkably simple. Except for the elephantine proportions of the milling machine itself, it occupies only a small corner of a large basement laboratory. All that can be seen is a modest row of six panels mounting nicely ordered banks of relays and vacuum tubes and a master timing mechanism. Behind this is a very small office with a drawing board or two, the automatic tape printer, and the playback machines pushed, like typewriters, into a corner. That is the whole thing.

In use, the machine requires no attention, once the metal workpiece is in place. In production runs, the bedplate is fitted with a jig so that workpieces can be slipped into the correct position in a minute or two. During the milling process the attendant has nothing to do but brush away the shavings and keep watch that no hitches develop. When the work is done, the machine stops itself, and the man lifts out the completed piece and puts in a fresh blank.

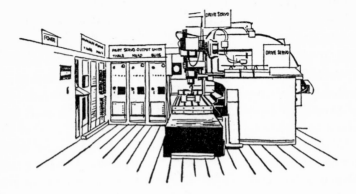

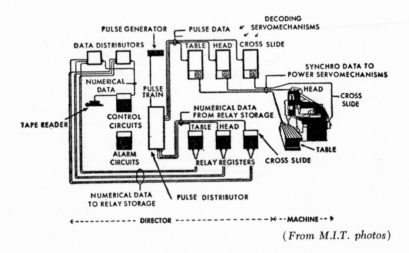

Diagram of M.I.T. automatic milling machine

The engineers who do the programming have nothing to do at all, once production has started. This might seem like a tremendous waste of brains, as well as of the attendant's manual skill. If the three men did nothing but tend this one machine it would be. In commercial practice, however, a shop would probably have several automatic tools of various kinds, and perhaps other types of automation. Then the three-man team would be kept busy operating them all at once.

In comparison to the conventional method of using skilled machinists, automatic equipment like this is sure to have a large advantage, especially in the smaller "job" shops where the runs on any one product are small. Here, the cost in skilled hand labor is very high, because the operator must first interpret his blueprints and scheme out the work he is to do. His schedule will include a large number of stops and resettings of the workpiece, only one cut for each setting. There may be dozens, each accompanied by slow, painstaking work in lining up and checking positions. Frequent stopping to measure and gauge the cuts will further extend production time. In a short run, the machine "down time"—when it is standing still—may be longer than the actual cutting time. This is the principal reason why machine shops charge very high hourly rates for their work.

On the automatic machine the piece is locked in and stays there, except in extremely complicated work. It neither has to be handled nor checked, once the first piece has come out right and proved that the machine is following directions.

A couple of years ago, M.I.T. gave an introductory course in automatic-machine operation to plant executives. One problem given the class was to program the milling machine for a small but insanely designed aluminum ash tray souvenir. The Laboratory had worked out a triangular shape with a sloping bottom and curves here and there that were pieces of elipses and hyperbolas. The rough blanks had been cast so as to require every surface to be milled out. It was about as difficult a cutting problem as could be devised. Just for comparison, they took the drawings around to various commercial shops and got bids on the cost of setting up the job. The bids ran up to $6000, for the first ash tray.

It turned out that no one in the executives' class was able to program the ash tray successfully; it required too much knowledge of mathematics and computer technique. However, the Laboratory had no trouble in doing it in about a day and a half. When the blanks had been cast—a routine foundry job—they were run through the milling machine to a finish in about 15 minutes each, and given away to the class as mementos. A test made with a shop machinist, working by hand from a standing start with the blueprints, showed that on the average it took him an hour and a half to machine each casting, exclusive of the time necessary to interpret the drawings.

The work done at M.I.T., and soon followed elsewhere, particularly at General Electric, has borne very definite fruit. Today, five heavy machinery builders are investigating the possibilities and at least one is in actual production. This is Giddings & Lewis, of Fond du Lac, Wisconsin. G & L have commercialized the computer-controlled machine along the lines described here, smoothing and refining the automatic features to look and work like modern office equipment. The master record of the operation to be performed is put on magnetic rather than paper tape. The tape spool is then taken to the shop, where it directs all machine operations from a single cabinet. The advantage of magnetic tape is that a sound track can be added. With this the programming can include spoken instructions to the attendant, alerting him to "planned stop" points in the operation, for changing tools on a complicated job, or for routine inspections.

The Barnes Engineering Company of Stamford, Connecticut, produces a computer device for complete automatic handling of standard lathe jobs. The whole apparatus is contained in a small cabinet no larger than a desk, which stands near the lathe.

The great virtue of this master-control system of automating conventional shop tools is that it is highly adaptable to short production runs. A serious limitation in shop automation is that the apparatus is so expensive that it cannot justify itself unless the output runs up to true mass-production figures. Yet a great deal of manufacturing today, particularly for the military, involves many short runs punctuated with incessant changes in the product design. With the application the M.I.T. Laboratory has made of computer fundamentals to machine control, short runs can be done economically, while changes are easy to incorporate by cutting out and substituting for portions of the paper or magnetic tape. At the same time, the machine becomes far more versatile than the cleverest human hands could make it.

8 | MARCH OF METAL

As a matter of contrast it will be interesting next to pay a visit to the celebrated Ford Engine Plant at Cleveland, Ohio, to see how the very large "frozen" type of automatic production works. This is the prime example of "Detroit automation," unique in the field because it is predominantly mechanical, and because a large part of the automatic feature is the handling and positioning of the product as it moves along the production line. Wholly unlike the automated shop machines, this gigantic display can do only one predetermined series of machine operations; it is virtually inflexible and any change in the product requires complete resetting of the entire line. It is strictly a mass-production scheme.

You come into a vast factory space that must be a quarter of a mile square, all under one roof. The first thing that strikes you is that there is so much machinery, so much rapid motion, so much noise, such a tangle of interwoven lines of progress, that the processes must certainly get in the way of each other. When you see that they do not, you realize what magnificent planning has been done, and how thoroughly the principles of automation have been exploited.

You catch a glimpse of long lines of engine blocks jerking and slamming along on roller conveyors. You will be looking at one idly, when suddenly it is seized by a maze of metal muscles, wrenched forward or back or turned end for end as if the mechanical genie behind it was in a fury. Not a second is lost; immediately another block has been driven home to the place the first one vacated. Some fifty or more behind it are jogged ahead to correspond.

Crowding and din do not seem to bother the machinery at all. People are the only ones who have to watch their step and stand clear. Your guide is at your elbow constantly, piloting you through narrow spaces walled with roaring giants that tower to the roof, pulling you out of the way of spurts of oil, steering you around piles of castings. The Ford engine line is something you won't soon forget.

In the mechanical innards of this howling birthplace of engines, you are witnessing the march of metal at the rate of 4500 engines a day—180 every hour of the 24. Every 20 seconds a casting weighing hundreds of pounds arrives from the foundry, is seized upon by a man using a mechanical gripper, and is skidded onto the open end of the roller track. Finished blocks, of course, are pouring out at the end of the line at a similar rate.

The purpose of the engine line is to prepare the rough casting—a single hunk of metal comprising cylinders and water jackets, crankshaft bearing supports and valve housings, part of the manifold passages—for the assembly line, where the gadgetry that makes an engine work is put on. Before reaching assembly there are more than 500 separate operations to be done on the casting, most of them with high precision. Possibly a hundred holes have to be drilled or reamed out, the cylinders bored and honed to a high polish, the base planed off true, and the casting tirelessly measured to see that no inaccuracy has crept in. All this is done upon an object far too heavy for a man to lift, at a speed far greater than he could manage, even if only his judgment were involved.

The raw casting first rolls into a checking station, where main dimensions are checked. Right off at the start, the machine knows whether a block is warped or twisted, so that it would choke the works later. If it fails on this inspection, it is switched off like a railroad car onto a siding, where it gets personal attention from one of the few human operators on the job. If the trouble is fixable, he skids the block off to a repair center, whence it eventually returns to join the parade. If the trouble is serious, the block will be condemned and returned to be melted up at the foundry.

Acceptable castings, the great majority, go sliding along toward their first major tussle with the great Gargantua, officially known as the Cross Transfermatic, in whose muscular grasp the first operations will be the planing of the engine base and the boring of the cylinders. Number One in the long array of prize-fighter-size machines picks the casting off the incoming line and thrusts it upside down into the dark interior, where you can glimpse a set of knives relentlessly chewing smoking shavings off the metal. That work takes only a minute, but a wild minute, punctuated by the squawk of protesting steel, the hiss of compressed air and the dull thunder of millions of foot-pounds of energy concentrated in one small spot. This is called *broaching*. The part of the machine that moves seems as big as the side of a house.

You are scarcely accustomed to this manhandling of metal when the block is suddenly expelled by mighty arms and sent clanking along the conveyor track toward its next ordeal. It is incredible, you think, that cast iron or anything else can take this brutal beating and still survive. The beauty of the engine line, of course, is that, among many other things, it knows just exactly how rough it can be with its victims without hurting them. Never a corner is knocked off nor a crack started.

The half-stunned visitor comes now to the boring and honing mills. Again the engine block is seized in sardonically gentle arms and tossed like a baby to a position high in the air, then swallowed into the digestive apparatus of the giant, a morsel of food for a whale. A gang of swirling spindles descends upon it, simultaneously rounding out all the cylinders at once. Down comes the casting again, and before it can compose itself it is injected into another boring mill, where a finer cut is taken, then into a third, for the delicate grinding operation and the honing, which leave the cylinder walls glass-smooth. If you have ever watched a garage mechanic working, working, working, hour by hour to fit new pistons into old engine cylinders, you will realize what automation can do in seconds, by contrast.

In all the activity you have witnessed so far, stretching perhaps over fifty feet, you have seen no more than half a dozen men. You wonder why there are any, since it is obviously impossible for a man to influence the megatherian efforts grinding steadily on in this iron jungle. But there lies the beauty and also the limitation of mechanical automation. Now and then the designers have thrust a human being's hand onto some little knob that can bring the whole vast complex to a halt with a single slight pressure. These men contribute the ultimate fine judgment to the machine. By sound, by sight, by feel, even by smell, they know at once if anything is amiss and can command Gargantua to wait. The judgment factor is exercised mostly in the matter of precise positioning of the block before each row of cutters descends upon it. Visible gauges and instruments help to verify this essential fact.

These so-called check points are manned by highly skilled and experienced people. Theirs is the responsibility for anticipating trouble, which might start in a triviality and end in a hash of hardware bigger than a city block.

Advocates of fully electronic automation sometimes joke about the heavy-handed Detroit variety by telling you that if anything happens along one of these engine lines, the blocks will begin to pile up and soon start pouring out of the shop windows into the yard. It looks as if this might happen, too, except that careful provisions are made to prevent it. These provisions are called "pools," or "floats." At various points there are switchyards in the conveyor system. If the line ahead is jammed full, the oncoming blocks simply turn up a side track and fill the float. From here on in, there are two parallel routes for the blocks to follow—two identical sets of machines doing like operations. Even this guarantee is not completely trusted. In addition there may be a reserve pool, reached by a branch line fed by hand. A man stands ready every minute to break in on the parade and divert some of it if need be.

The traffic layout here reminds you of a city intersection at rush hour, the cops without uniforms but with long steel hooks. Such a hook might be very useful, indeed, to thin out a sticky mass of automobiles, which seem to behave as stupidly as these blocks do. Again a point in the line where just a touch of human judgment gives automation that final spark of necessary vigor.

The cause of traffic jams on the engine line are mainly two. A block may be just a fraction at fault in some dimension so that it fails to "register" with the handling machinery. Or the cutting tools within the giants themselves may get dull, snag or break. The preventive measure for the first is repeated automatic gauging operations at strategic points. That for the second is an iron-rigid schedule of tool replacement before they reach old age.

Every machine has been figured most carefully for the number of cuts it can take without wearing out its keen cutting edges. The machine itself keeps count, and when the time for routine change approaches, it lights a warning light on the "toolmeter" panel at the maintenance superintendent's station. Regular shutdown periods are allowed for all units in the line, and all designated tools are removed and replaced. If a tool breaks—even the giant's teeth sometimes have their flaws—a single machine can always be taken out of action without stalling the line if proper switching operations are used.

It is not to be thought that the machines do their stuff blindly. Far from it. A highly complex arrangement of electronic gauges, position-checkers, error-detectors of many kinds is built in, to form a specialized computer for the one job of making engine blocks that can all be relied upon to behave alike when they finally get on the road. Twenty-five miles of wiring are needed to make the whole thing work. There is nothing hit-or-miss about any of it. The "brain" has been instructed in advance in every possible detail. Through its sensing organs it can tell whether the work it has done is up to standard, whether it must take still another cut, or must signal that the block it is working on has got out of hand and should be withdrawn for special human attention.

As you move gingerly along beside the engine line, you find that the operations are getting somewhat smaller and more precise. After the brute-force work of beating the block down to near-size, comes a long series of truing-up operations and the boring, reaming, and counterboring of the myriad holes the block requires. It is here that you come face to face with the device that gives this great conglomerate its name: the "transfer table."

No matter what kind of a job is to be done by a machine tool upon a piece of metal, it cannot start until the workpiece is perfectly positioned for cutting. In non-automated shops the set-up time may be as long or longer than the actual working time on the machine. The bigger and more complicated the piece, the more securely and carefully it must be held. Tool pressures of tons may be exerted upon it, and it cannot yield in any direction by a measurable amount or it will ruin the cut that is to be taken. Automobile engines are notoriously demanding in this, for they are high-precision machines. The greatest triumph of Detroit automation—in fact, the secret of the whole thing—is its ability to seize a great mass of irregular metal, recognize its shape and "geography," then twist it, turn it, invert it, lay it on its side or cater-cornered in some fashion, and present it to the cutting tools with approximately no error in position.

As we mentioned earlier, Ford has described automation as "the automatic handling of parts between progressive production processes." Although this seemed confusing and a little vague at first, now, in the presence of the engine line itself, it becomes quite clear. To position a piece of metal accurately in one machine after another is not enough. It must be transported between stations, often receiving the preliminary reorientation while it is on the way. In factories where there is no Detroit automation, this transport work is laboriously done by hand or by hand-controlled transporters such as trucks, dollies, cranes, or isolated conveyors. Arrived at the next working station, it is lifted off its carrier, often by a chain-hoist or small hand crane, and dangled into the new machine, whereupon one or more men jockey it sweatingly into place.

Nothing like this could be tolerated in a plant that turns out 4500 engines a day. The engine blocks move like the elements of a fluid, continuously. No human hand touches them, nor are they loaded onto anything or picked up and put down by anything except the one machine itself. The procession of blocks moves on, incessantly, shoulder to shoulder, and its travel includes repeated preparations for each subsequent ordeal.

At the head of the line, where the gigantic boring and broaching machines work, the interval between operations is short—a few feet—and the block is mauled and manhandled continuously, like a man falling afoul of a gang of mobsters in a dark alley. When one set of massive arms swings the block down and out of one machine, a hydraulic ram nudges it directly into the rack that will lift it into the next machine. The chances are that this second operation will call for a different position of the block. For instance, the first treatment, broaching of the engine base, is done upside down. The cylinder boring, on the other hand, is done at an angle. So, as the metal piece is relinquished by the broach, it is turned over. Actually, the whole rack which grips it flops over on its own bearings, advances its passenger to the waiting arms of the boring mill, uncouples itself and retires. The new carrier, almost before you can catch it in action, has clamped down on the block, hoisted it up maybe ten feet, and inserted it onto tracks within the machine.

You don't see what happens next: it is out of sight. But the gist of it is that, with the block now sitting in its new position, groups of feelers come at it from all sorts of angles, testing to see whether it has arrived in the precisely correct position, measuring its location in relation to the cutters. This is a feedback operation. The machine has memory. It compares the messages from its feelers with the standards it knows are required and keeps on jockeying and testing till those standards are fully met. If a man did all this, it might take him hours of trial and error. Gargantua enjoys poking a 200-pound engine block into place in a couple of seconds.

Later on, as the block emerges from the cavern of giants into the small forest of boring mills, hole tappers, and reamers—those hundreds of trimming operations that finish the job—the transfer tables stand out more noticeably. You can see the long line of engine blocks edging along on their roller track, right-side-up, perhaps. Suddenly there is a clank and a clatter. A block has been captured by the table, uncannily, for it is not easy to see what snatched it or what decided it to do it. At any rate, it is jerked into a kind of open-work steel frame. Bars and slides find familiar bearing points on the casting. Sometimes "registering dowels" descend into holes or cavities already in the block. In a jiffy the piece is imprisoned, completely restrained. The transfer table knows exactly where it is and what aspect it presents. Then comes the spin-around. The next operation, apparently, wants it end-for-end. Clang! The block is turned, shoved forward, jacked over a foot or so, and pushed smoothly onto the waiting machine.

The table loses interest immediately. With a slight whirring of gears it withdraws its tentacles and sits motionless and watchful, waiting for the moment to seize its next candidate.

This transfer table is one of the most ingenious and typical of American inventions. Ever since Eli Whitney and the cotton gin, intricate mechanical motions have had a fascination for us. We love to rig up outlandish trains of gears, shafts, spindles, cams, rockers, fingers, cranks, wheels, slides—all hung together in an amazingly friendly union that never misses a beat. One part moves, triggering another; something lifts, touching off something else that turns. A grabber rises out of the welter, grabs something, turns a little, deposits it, sinks into the jungle again. This is Detroit automation, expressing its genius through the transfer table.

Fifteen minutes staring at a transfer table at work and you wonder why you have always thought Rube Goldberg's concoctions were so insane. A good deal of the fascination lies in the very thing that the cartoonist has exploited: that sardonic similarity between these insanely ingenious machines and people. Thousands, touring the Ford line every year, sigh, "Why, it's almost human!" If to be human were to possess the ability to handle tons of metal with supreme accuracy at lightning speed, then the cliché would have some meaning. Automation is a bid for burying that old chestnut for good.

Nevertheless the thing does *act* human—a true robot in the sense that Capec dreamed it—an iron man with muscles and the sense to use them for meaningful ends. He picks things up in his fists, a dozen of them at once, and entwines them with a score of fingers. He embraces things with arms from all sides and kicks them over with a baker's dozen of feet. He can blow, or stretch, or crush, or twist, and whatever he does he does just right, neither gently nor brutally, but with precisely the force required to accomplish his task. He is an incongruous lampoon of humanity, and the joke is on us if we don't realize that the brain he is using is a corner of our own.

Detroit, being the cradle of mass production, was naturally the birthplace of these versatile metal men who need only electric power and a little lubrication to continue their work indefinitely. Men, indeed, who are neat as well as efficient, for they carefully clean away their refuse of steel shavings and used-up oil and send it, nicely packaged, back to the foundry. Among the originators of these humanized monsters, the names of the Hautau brothers and of Cross loom large—two groups of superlatively ingenious men who set out, after the war, to prove that machines must take over if men were to get back their birthright of freedom from slavery. Their work, and the work of countless engineers and skilled operators and maintenance men, has become an essential ingredient in the production of millions of cars and billions of car parts every year.

As for the Ford engine plant, and those similar ones of Chevrolet and Chrysler, one could go on finding new details to gape at almost indefinitely. The great contribution of them all, it seemed to this observer, is their magnificent co-ordination. Not their individual superhuman machines, not their innumerable transfer tables, not their uncannily responsible automatic checkers and aligners, but their serene integration of all these things into a system that *works*. A system that has replaced the old one, run by 400 men, with a new one that functions faster with a tenth as many; a system that *can* make the cars we need at the price we can pay, where men surely could not. A system, it must be admitted, that will probably end up in a museum as electronics gradually takes over.

Awaiting that day, the automotive industry goes on automating its lines, well aware that it is buying speed and quality at enormous cost, the greatest part of which is the fact that the engine line is frozen to one product in one style and of one rigid set of dimensions. These giants are specialists. Flexibility is a thing they can't have.

9 | STEEL—LIFEBLOOD OF THE WESTERN WORLD

The job that automation has to do in industry divides itself pretty definitely into the mass-production of millions of identical pieces, on the one hand, and the delivery of a homogeneous fluid that flows out at the finish end in bulk. Although steelmaking has many different products, it is in many phases a fluid-producing industry. For you can make a rod, a bar, a sheet, or a pipe, not in lengths but in reels or rolls, and keep the mills that disgorge them turning them out without a stop. Short lengths can then be cut to suit the market. Thus, steelmaking is a natural candidate for automation, where continuity of production is the paramount issue for speed and economy.

In spite of Evans' Revolutionary flour mill, none of the fluid-type industries—oil, gas, chemicals, grains, steel—began as a continuous-flow process. They were all worked by the batch method, the brew concocted on the kitchen stove. They kept on at this, by sheer conventionality, until economic pressure forced the change-over. While ripe for the switch, steel was slower than most because of tradition and the gigantic forces that nature requires to make it.

The steelmaking art disappears into the fog of old centuries. It has always been work for human giants; the tough, resourceful fighters against brute nature. These were men lined up with bare hands against tons of weight, against bulk greater than a whole house, against temperatures known rarely outside the sun. And yet the art was leavened with a dash of precise chemistry and physics. Any old combination of iron and carbon won't make steel. Hit-or-miss cooking of the melt brings failure. You can't roll steel that is too hot or too cold. You can't send it to market unannealed. Precision creeps in everywhere along with giantism.

A tradition of artistry has grown up with the business. These were men who had muscle but also fine judgment, hairline skills in determining when to blow, when to skim, scarf, and pour. Truly a trade of most exacting demands, the more so because huge amounts of half-finished materials could be ruined by a single wrong step. It is not surprising that archaic hand methods survived even in the American steelmaking industry at least until the nineteen-twenties. Thereafter, it is interesting to see, steel stepped out ahead as a leader in automatic operation and, in some instances, as a pioneer in automation itself. It was not a leadership that received much publicity. In the murk of the vast mill sheds, little change could be seen by the few outsiders who came to observe.

The change-over—and it was very gradual—began with the shifting of extreme muscular effort from the backs of men to the backs of machines. Ladles of molten metal, billets of white-hot steel, snaking wires, and shapes of all kinds had been handled by men with the most primitive of tools. Now, gigantic tongs and grippers and rolls took the brute handling jobs away from them. Little by little the old-timers faded out of the picture and men of less strength but superior skill took their places. Mechanization meant that it made little difference how hot or how heavy a chunk of steel might be. The physical effort—and the ever-present danger—of controlling it was practically nil.

Automatic steelmaking machinery came next, and with it the start of the continuous process. In those older days sheet, for example, had been made in small pieces. Two small bars of metal were heated in the furnace, rolled, sheared, folded and doubled, heated again, rolled once more, then separated, "pickled," annealed, rolled one last time, cold, and delivered to the shipping room. Some figures will illustrate how this compares with what is done now, after full mechanization.

When steel sheet was made the old way, in a "hand hot mill," seven men could produce about 11 tons of finished sheet in a single work-shift. Today, with the most modern of automated equipment, the same number of men will turn out some 550 tons of finished product per shift—a fifty-fold increase. In the hand hot mill, seventy-pound bars were generally used to start the process; a man could not handle any more without risk to his life and danger of botching the job. Now, it is common to see billets of 15 tons go through into the rollers of a modern strip mill. The product in those days was a pile of sheets about the size of a bedspread. Modern strip comes out of the mill shed in a huge roll weighing tons and stretching thousands of feet in one piece.

The reason for this vast improvement in production is easy to see. Where the old system required many dozens of handling operations, the new system requires only one or two: feeding the mill the billet and removing the finished goods.

This sweeping modernization has not been all plain sailing, nor is the mill itself any simpler than in the old days. It goes through the same general steps of forming massive billet down into thin sheet. Each "pass," or rolling down from one thickness to a lesser one, must be controlled with unwavering precision. Add the fact that production requires speeds of forty miles an hour or more of the racing steel, and you have a complicated situation for automatic control to handle.

The old-timers had a hard time with it. The seven-man crew that now presides over a roaring strip mill are not workmen-artists but managers, with heavy responsibility for making accurate judgments and decisions under extreme pressure of time. In the old days, a man made steel as fast as he could do it well and no faster, taking what time he needed for each decision, producing at a uniform rate commensurate with his skill. In the new day, the operator sits in a little cubicle high above the floor, surrounded by an array of levers, buttons and warning lights, and is truly a slave to his machine. A single misstep on his part and scrap may roll out by the ton.

Steelmaking has bought itself tremendous production speed but has put mental strains on human beings that they cannot always bear.

There is an old story of the Bessemer furnace that points up this burden of responsibility. Like a giant pitcher with no handle, the Bessemer sat on trunnions, with its mouth elevated and a blast of air roaring up from the bottom to smelt the mass of iron, coke, and scrap to just the right chemical composition. The "blower," one of the most skillful of the artisans of that day, watched the mighty flame at the converter's mouth; when its color exactly suited him, he signaled his crew to overturn the furnace and pour. Some blowers were not too good at this. If they missed, the whole melt was ruined.

But there was a mule that dragged the big ladle into position for the pour. Tradition had it that if the blower didn't know when to pour he could simply wait for the mule to come plodding up with the ladle. The animal always knew when the crucial moment had come.

Today, the Bessemer converter still has its mule—an automated gadget whose heart is a photoelectric cell sharply sensitive to the color required at pouring time. The blower is still there, and he checks the device against long experience. His main job now is to know what to do with variations in the melt. He knows the chemistry of steel, and it is his superior judgment that counts, from one batch to another. Giving the routine decision to the electronic gadget has freed him for a higher activity. And saved his eyes from a most dangerous duty, too.

All through the modern steel mill you find mechanical replacements like this, and the consequent upgrading of the men. Art is yielding to science. But it is yielding slowly. There are still many processes where the older methods of batch handling have persisted, and where automation is having a hard fight to get in. The blast-furnace reduction of iron ore to pig, the coking of coal, the making and pouring of the huge ingots with which begin all steel production, the fabricating of heavy beams and rails—all of these are candidates for automatic control; all have some, but not nearly enough to call it automation. That is why, in our brief visit to a steel mill, we shall stick to the strip mill, in which automation has gone the farthest.

Quite as important as high speed of production and uniformity of results is the quality of the product. Steel is a fiercely competitive industry, not only within itself but with other metals. It must turn out its uniform best with every ton. This is another reason why the nearly instantaneous decisions, how hot, how thick, how fast, must be delegated to automatic control devices. No two men have quite the same judgment in like circumstances. With men making the routine decisions, the product would be slightly different in each shift on a single day.

Let's take a look at a typical tin-plate mill such as you would see if you visited a large steel company. Plate is the steel sheet out of which tin cans are made. You can get an idea of how fast the whole process must be when you realize that tin cans are formed out of the silvery sheet material at the rate of 475 a minute, by a single standard machine. And there are hundreds of them working in all parts of the country. Some of them are making experimental runs at the rate of 800 cans a minute. That is better than 13 cans a second—three for every tick of a bedroom clock.

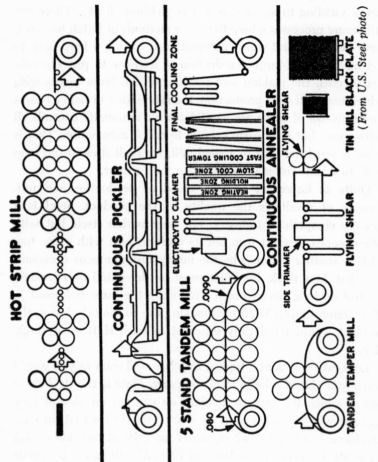

Diagram of a tin-plate mill

(*From U.S. Steel photo*)

It would be quite impossible to supply the steel for this insatiable automatic monster without a considerable degree of automation in the tin-plate mill itself. W. K. Scott, an engineer in the San Francisco division of U.S. Steel, tells us some of the factors which make it possible to manufacture the steel for those cans. He lists them this way:

1. We have a continuous process.
2. We convey the product automatically between various machines and processes.
3. The process is completely mechanized.
4. A mill such as this employs many self-correcting regulating systems constantly checking for operational variations.
5. The production of nearly 10,000 tons a day is supervised by very few men along the mill train—it varies from mill to mill, averaging about 25 to 28 people in the direct operating crew from the furnaces to coil storage.

Some of the latest technological developments are found on these mills:

1. The X-ray thickness gauge in a number of positions along the mill is able to detect product thickness, which can then be observed on remote indicators and recorders.
2. The infra-red-radiation width gauge permits closer adherence to commercial tolerances and improved yield.
3. The industrial television installation on the runout table gives the finisher a close view of strip configuration and camber. It is a great benefit in minimizing cobbles on coiler guides.

Mr. Scott adds modestly that "various features are under development by major steel companies to make the hot-strip-mill process even more automatic." * A modern hot-strip mill, he says, may have a million dollars' worth of electronic equipment on it. Such a mill can produce more than three million tons of finished tin-plate steel in a year. There are mills like this in many parts of the United States.

* W. K. Scott, in a speech before the Symposium on Electronics and Automatic Production, San Francisco, August 22, 1955.

The tin-plate process is divided into a long series of separate operations, beginning with bars of white-hot steel and ending with stacks of rectangular sheets, plated and ready for the can-makers. The steel thins down from several inches in thickness to about 1/100th of an inch. It picks up a coating of pure tin on both sides some ninety millionths of an inch thick, every bit of which must be inspected for pinholes and blemishes.

The strip mill itself is a series of rolling stands passing the steel through at racing speed, controlled at many points by guides and detectors which exert correcting forces to keep it in line. Thickness gauges watch it constantly. The readings of all these automatic devices are brought out onto meters on a small console at the end of the line, where the mill boss watches production from minute to minute. Six other men stand guard over the six stages of rolling along the way.

As the sheet comes out, it passes under a group of water sprays which cool it off to room temperature. It then goes on to the reeler and is wound up in a great roll weighing many tons. Here is a definite break in the continuity, for the next job of "pickling" is slow and requires four parallel lines to keep up production speed.

Pickling of newly rolled steel is necessary to remove the iron oxide mill scale which has accumulated during the hot working. It cannot be allowed to go on into the finished product, for the steel would not be strong or uniform and it would not plate. Pickling is done in tanks with strong chemical solutions, and the installation takes up a vast space. The rolls of strip from the mill are fed into advancing rollers at the head end of each line by hand, and from there on automation does the rest. This work used to be done on sheets already cut. The men picked up all they could carry and placed them one at a time in racks which were then lowered into tanks. Today, the pickling line takes just about as many operators as formerly, but the production is four to six times as much in the same time.

The pickling process leaves the steel bright and clean and dry, automatically packaged once more into the same huge rolls. We now come to what seemed to me, as I visited the Pittsburgh plant of the Jones & Laughlin Steel Company, to be the most fascinating part of the whole operation. This is the *cold* rolling of the material down to final thickness. Cold rolling is needed to swedge the metal into a compact and strong product. It is done on a behemoth known as a "five-stand tandem mill," which looms about as high as a two-story house and covers as much territory. Like the other stages before it, this one accepts the steel in rolled-up form and delivers it the same way. The material enters with a thickness of eight hundredths of an inch and emerges at nine thousandths—almost a ten-to-1 reduction.

In the tandem mill we get real drama, for, as anyone knows who has pounded a nail, cold steel does not deform easily. To begin with, the mill makes a deafening noise which gets into your chest and shakes your whole body. This is not surprising, for the strip of metal is being seized and flashed through the mill at nearly 60 miles an hour. Some mills are capable of 7000 feet per minute—close to 80 miles an hour.

You note with amazement that a roll of steel, starting into the mill six or eight feet in diameter, is being swallowed up so fast that it is gone while you watch. With uncanny precision the flashing metal whips around as if in a nightmare. If it ever got away . . . But it doesn't. It rests on rollers in a depression in the floor and is well guarded. The six men who superintend the mill pay it no attention, but they are never far from the bank of control buttons and instruments. Sometimes they chat pleasantly in sign language or yell in each other's ears. The mill looks out for itself completely, even to reaching out and grabbing a new roll of steel when an old one has been lashed through.

In many ways this headlong machine beats the automotive engine line because it is an outstanding example of hairline control of sheer brute force. Let's see how fine that control must be. The steel goes in with a thickness of about 1/10th of an inch and comes out ten times as thin, *but no wider*. This means that it must be elongated to ten times its original length. Since the elongation takes place in five stages of rolling, each stage represents a jump in speed and a different rate of spinning for each set of rollers. If all the rollers could turn at the same speed, they could be geared together. As it is, they are independent, each driven by its own giant electric motor. These stages, or "stands," however, must be absolutely matched in relative speed. One pair must not produce thinned steel faster (or slower) than the next pair can accommodate it. A loop of metal forming between pairs at high speed would wreck the mill and very likely the plant as well.

Down inside the machine, guarding against this, is one of the best examples of what automation can do to provide instantaneous control. Consecutive pairs of rollers are so timed that the strip of steel between them maintains a definite tension at all times. This tension, therefore, is the physical quantity that must be measured and held constant. Between stands of rollers, a small single roller rides the strip, free to turn but held in contact with the steel by a hinged frame that can move up and down. At the right tension, the strip sags slightly under the weight of the free roller and the roller rides in the "lap" of this sag, dropping slightly as tension diminishes, rising again when the tension mounts. A delicate measure of tension is thus provided by the *position* of the free roller and its frame.

Attached to the frame is a variable electrical resistance, which produces an electric voltage in a circuit that is exactly proportional to the strip tension. This voltage, maybe enough to light a common flashlight, is sent to another room to control the thousands of horsepower that drive the mill. Each set of rollers has its own tension-measuring device and so, though all are independent, all work in the right speed relation to each other.

Now we go into the motor room to see how the tiny signals are "blown up" to real power.

The room is separate and runs along behind the tandem mill, with the motor shafts protruding through the wall. It is completely filled with electrical machinery—little motors and big ones, small generators and large. Rows of intricate panels line the walls, many of them with electronic tubes faintly glowing on them. Here, too, the noise is deafening, but it is the whine of electrical machinery, not the clatter of steel.

Our signals from each tension-measurer outside have come in onto the panels over small wires. Here they are amplified and built up into power enough to control small motors which drive the generators installed in long rows on the floor. The control of direct-current electric motors is accomplished by feeding more or less voltage to their field windings, thus manipulating the strength of the magnetic poles which urge the rotating "armatures" around. A small voltage change is enough to make a large difference in the power put out by the motor. Hence, power amplification is easy to accomplish.

The team of motor-generators that serves any one stand of the mill is composed of several stages, the generator current of one stage manipulating the magnetic field of the motor in the next. Each set is larger than the one before it, till the final stage feeds a main generator which directly supplies the roller-driving motor for that stand of the mill. The dramatic contrast is that the fractional flea power of the incoming signal is faithfully reproduced in many thousands of horsepower with all the fine variations required by the tension of the speeding strip of steel. The whole thing operates with the precision of a wrist watch.

More dramatic still, if for any reason there is a jam-up, the operator need only touch a red button on his panel and the whole roaring giant will come to a dead stop in four seconds, by means of electric braking. It can be put back at full speed in eight. Little invisible streams of electrons accomplish it all in millionths of a second. A job, indeed, utterly beyond human capabilities.

This much automation is virtually standard in all big mills, but it is not complete. Steel men speak hopefully of "full" automatic operation and are experimenting with it. A radioisotope thickness gauge is the next step—two of them, in fact: at the first and last stages of the tandem mill. Not only will they record the strip thickness continuously. They will also be connected to screw-down motors which will raise or lower the rollers to maintain uniformity of the product.

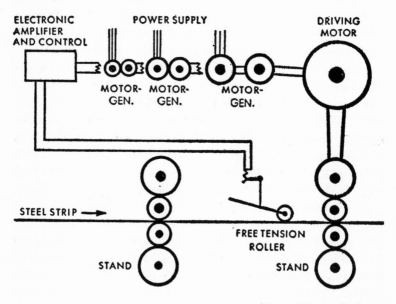

(*From U.S. Steel photo*)

Typical tandem mill strip-tension control

There is further automatic handling of the strip on its way to becoming tin plate. After cold rolling it gets an annealing treatment in a unit as high as a six-story office building, and several other treatments that end up with the "tin line." The plating can be handled in either of two ways: by electrolytic deposit of the pure tin onto the steel in one continuous strip, or by cutting the strip into rectangular sheets and sending them through a bath of the molten plating metal in a continuous end-to-end *stream*. In either method, electronic guardians watch every step, detecting pinholes in the plating, watching thickness of plate. This is quite a delicate matter, considering that the plating is less than one ten-thousandth of an inch deep. The final watchdog is called a "self-correcting regulator"—a feedback gadget that superintends the whole line behind it and makes corrections at any point that is out of step. These regulators are far faster than humans would be, and more dependable. As Scott says, "they are tireless and will make corrections in operation no matter how hot the day or how minute the variation."

Strangely enough, the last of all the operations is an inspection done by human eye, un-automated. Tomorrow that, too, will fall within the province of electronic machines. The job, now commonly done by a battalion of girls, consists of close scrutiny of every inch of a plated piece for surface defects. The girls have been trained to a wizardry of swift judgment that is unerring. A tin-can manufacturer cannot allow defects to creep into his product.

Automation in tin-plate inspection will be done with a "flying-spot scanner," now in experimental use. This is an application of television. As the sheets to be inspected hurry along on a conveyor belt at the rate of 1500 feet per minute, a streak of bright light rides across each one, embracing its whole width. The bright tin coat reflects this bar of light into two TV camera tubes. Any blemish will appear to the tube as a dark spot on its screen. To cover every element of a wide plate moving by

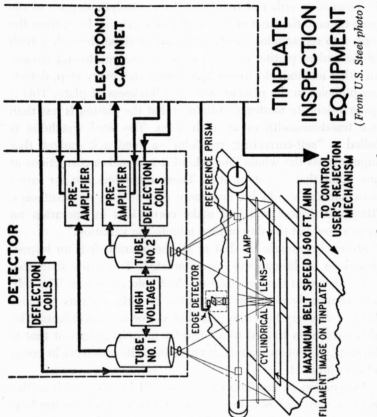

Diagram of tin-plate automated inspection device

DETECTOR

DEFLECTION COILS

TUBE NO. 1

HIGH VOLTAGE

TUBE NO. 2

PRE-AMPLIFIER

PRE-AMPLIFIER

DEFLECTION COILS

ELECTRONIC CABINET

EDGE DETECTOR

REFERENCE PRISM

LAMP

CYLINDRICAL LENS

FILAMENT IMAGE ON TINPLATE

MAXIMUM BELT SPEED 1500 FT./MIN

TO CONTROL USER'S REJECTION MECHANISM

TINPLATE INSPECTION EQUIPMENT

(From U.S. Steel photo)

at some 17 miles an hour, the scanning beams of the tubes must travel back and forth at 25,000 miles an hour in one direction and at about 100,000 miles an hour in the other. Again, electrons think nothing of it.

Many people, even many businessmen, still make light of automation and feel that it is overrated. In a few industries this may be true. In a tremendous task like steel, however, no man is able to produce quantities so great or control machines so vast as can be achieved by the insignificant little gadgets already spotted about in the dim caverns of the mills. The routine but vital decisions that produce steel of top quality today are for automation to do. The men's job is to invent and build and master-mind the machines.

10 | CINDERELLA'S SLIPPER

It's a far cry from steel to shoes and from the split-second automation of cold-rolled strip to the nearly total lack of it in the shoemaking business. Yet shoes seem to fit in here because of their very wealth of contrast. We have had two outstanding examples of products which the public could not even buy without benefit of automatic manufacture. Let's see how well one of the most universal articles in the world is doing without it.

If the remnants of tradition still cling to steel, shoes are up to their necks in it. Footwear is no longer made by cobblers, but the cobblers are still there, working in shoe factories, a great number of which are brick buildings well on toward a hundred years old. These factories have plenty of machinery, some of which is modern and efficient. It is rather like textile machinery, ingenious, "automatic," fast. Actually, it is no more automatic than a sewing machine. Indeed, shoemaking is still essentially a sewing and nailing job, strictly dependent upon the skill and judgment of the people who do it.

Shoe-factory workers are among the poorest paid artisans in America. The reason given is that they do not contribute very much to our over-all economy. They are really in a class with seamstresses. Skill they have, but it is a skill anyone can master quickly. Fifty or sixty dollars a week is about all a shoeshop worker can hope for.

However, the shoe manufacturer does not have an easy time either. His industry is one of the most unintegrated on the commercial map. Its independent units resemble the little principalities of Germany in the days before unification. There are literally hundreds of small walled citadels of shoemaking, all in fierce competition. An estimated half-billion shoes are made every year in the United States, but the largest single run on one style is in the neighborhood of 80,000 pairs.

The shoe field is strictly a buyer's market. There are far too many styles, shapes, and materials, far too many manufacturers. Most orders run to no more than a few dozen pairs. Sometimes the Army or Navy buys up 50,000 pairs at once. Nobody else would dream of it. But no shoe manufacturer can be sure of this, so he maintains almost double the manufacturing capacity that he actually uses. This makes investment costs in machinery inordinately high; naturally, it keeps old-fashioned equipment on duty far beyond its best days. Compared to radio and tin-can making, shoemaking seems like a throwback to the middle ages.

This is not the fault of anyone in particular. The human foot is the real cause—an item of infinite variety. Human preference and vanity also play a big part, especially on the feminine side. Much of the disorganization in the industry stems from women's impatience with frozen styling. Shoe designers, straining to keep up, are constantly putting out new models to pique the feminine taste. No one really knows whether the chicken or the slipper came first.

The industry might accommodate itself to this shifting demand if it were not that shoe *thinking*, technically speaking, is really of the Dark Ages. The system of dividing shoes into sizes and widths is in serious need of repair. Within a single style pattern, there may be scores of different sizes and widths, which the industry calls "grades." They bear a relation to each other which is unhappily at variance with the present-day mathematics of machines. Grades differ from one another according to a strictly rule-of-thumb formula which is rigid throughout the trade and is nearly impossible to mechanize effectively. The formula is deceptively simple. It merely says that as you go from one size to the next larger, you add 1/3rd inch to the length of a shoe, 1/4th inch to its girth, and 1/12th inch to its width. Offhand, this looks fine, as it did to King Edward II of England, who invented it.

The story goes that in the year 1324 the king decreed that three barley corns, taken from the center of the ear and placed end to end, should equal one "inch." Among the first things to be measured by this new unit was the length of the human foot. It turned out that the largest normal British foot measured 39 barley corns long, or 13 inches. Hence this foot was arbitrarily called a size 13. The scale of sizes was then graded down from this, a barley corn at a time; in other words, in steps of 1/3rd inch.

In more modern times, the use of the barley-corn unit was abandoned for width and girth, because it was too large. One-fourth and one-twelfth inch increments were chosen in order to retain somewhere near the proportions of a given model in all sizes. It has worked out very well for the purchaser of shoes, but rather badly for the makers. Adding or subtracting fixed amounts to an object of three dimensions does not preserve its original shape at the extremes of size. It cannot be made to do so.

Shoe men illustrate the difficulty with the analogy of the photographic enlargement. A picture, when "blown up" on a screen or print, retains its correct proportions absolutely. All dimensions are increased in the same ratio, giving complete verisimilitude. Objects and people look familiar and normal no matter how large or how small. Enlarging by this means is called *geometric*, and it is the only way that light, shining through a symmetrical lens, can do it. If you attempted to add fixed amounts to each picture dimension, instead of proportional amounts, you would need a mathematician to design the apparatus; such a machine would produce the weird distortions of a crazy mirror in an amusement park. The short dimensions would be doubled, while the long ones would hardly be affected at all.

Yet this is just about what happens in the shoe industry. A design is drawn up by an artist, with fine attention to "composition" and symmetry. A model is made of this by a skilled carver of wood, and the shoe is on its way. The model-maker chooses a size about midway in the scale, and his work is copied into a long series of wooden "lasts," using the rule-of-thumb formula to create the various grades. This is known in the trade as the *arithmetic* system.

Subtle changes take place in the design. A skinny shoe gets skinnier as it gets bigger and stubbier as it gets smaller. At the extreme ends of the scale—known to the industry as the "tariff"—the model has become a caricature of itself, with strongly distorted proportions. Again, it is not the buyer who cares very much; it is the designer and manufacturer, who cannot turn out clear-cut styles and so must produce many styles to satisfy the public taste.

The maker's problem is one of producing a large number of different shoes, none of which will enjoy much sale. To do this he has to make lasts in all possible grades and in all popular styles—hundreds and thousands of them. No shoe can be made except upon a last. The last, as an old saying goes, comes first.

The last is a pattern of hard wood, shaped approximately like a foot, up to the ankle bone. There must be a right one and a left one for each pair of shoes, though of course many thousand pairs of shoes can be built upon one pair of lasts. This pattern determines the exact shape of the interior of the shoe, for it is put on a machine and the shoe is constructed tightly around it. If there are 200 or more grades to be made from a single style model, there will have to be 200 or more *pairs* of lasts. Which makes the last, and its inflexible system of sizing, a major headache in the trade.

Lasts are produced on a special lathe which rotates a block of wood slowly, while a cutting tool shaves off the excess and produces the complicated curved surface desired. The cutter itself moves irregularly, being linked through a series of steel arms to a doughnut-shaped steel roller which steadily contacts the model. This, in turn, is rotating at the same speed as the wood being cut. Cutter and follower move ahead together, down the length of the last from heel to toe. The final result is a duplicate of the last.

Complicated linkages are needed to introduce the fractional-inch increments needed to make the last larger or smaller than the model. A great deal of ingenuity has gone into engineering the last-lathe, and it is an expensive piece of equipment. It does represent, however, a successful mechanization of a very awkward problem. Perhaps the most technical part of the shoe industry is the last factory, where the wooden forms are turned out by the thousand for sale to the actual makers of shoes.

There is a considerable contribution of personal skill in the making of a tariff of lasts, and they are seldom completely uniform. This variation carries over to the shoemaking machinery, and the operator of it again contributes a generous personal share, just as a seamstress does by the way she feeds the cloth into her sewing machine. It would be very nearly impossible to design an automated shoemaking line to accommodate the lasts as they are made today. No two would meet the stiff requirements of uniformity posed by an automatic machine. Thus it can be seen that whatever of automation may concern the shoe industry must be in the future. Left to themselves, the manufacturers would probably go on indefinitely at the old stand. And as the cost of labor and materials went up, the price of shoes would go up, too.

The United Shoe Machinery Corporation, a principal maker of shoe-building machines, is now taking the position that this uneconomical system should be scrapped in favor of one solidly founded on engineering mathematics. The company is sure that automation is possible, but not until something has been done to regularize the last. Simply stated—it is really not simple— USMC proposes to change the centuries-old method of arithmetic grading of shoes to the geometric one. Given a single style model, all sizes of this particular design will then be identical in *proportions*. The USMC laboratories have already taken the first step by designing and building a machine to cut geometric lasts from a model, and by actually setting up a pilot shoe-making line to prove that the principle is sound.

An immediate improvement has been demonstrated. From a single model, turned out by the designer and wood-carver, all possible lasts, both rights and lefts, can be turned out at greatly improved production speeds. The lathe which makes the lasts now operates on the familiar pantograph principle. The arm which transmits the following motion of the roller on the model to the last-cutting tool becomes the familiar scissors-like linkage of the well-known pantograph devices used in shops and on drawing boards everywhere.

The method of making rights and lefts is interesting. The present old-fashioned system requires that a right and a left model be made by the design shop, one for each foot. In the new system the lathe is hooked up so that it normally makes a last for the foot *opposite* to the one represented by the model. When this last is done, it is used for a model itself and the lathe produces its opposite, or the mate to the first last. This neat trick is possible because geometric reproduction is so accurate that one last can be a model for another without error. A single model is thus sufficient for the right and left lasts of all

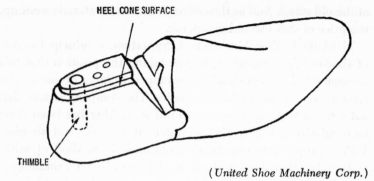

HEEL CONE SURFACE

THIMBLE

(*United Shoe Machinery Corp.*)

Two-part geometric last with "intelligence plate"

grades of a shoe, and all will be in perfect conformity with the
model, whatever the size. There must, however, be a different
model for each *width*, since the proportions change with each
of them.

The real opportunity for shoe automation begins with the
completion of the geometric last—a mathematically perfect
guide for a machine to follow. The present arithmetic last is
not exact enough for this, although it is not a serious drawback
so long as there is a human operator to contribute the personal
touch which trues each shoe up. With the geometric last, a machine can be built and programmed to carry out all the operations to make a shoe. It won't be a simple machine but it can
be made.

The secret of automation will reside in the last, actually in a
single feature, an "intelligence plate," screwed to the top of
the last heel. This is a piece of metal about the size of a small
business card, but 1/4th inch thick. It carries a central hole
very carefully located, into which the "jacks" or mounting pins
of the various automated machines will fit. This hole is always
located in the same relation to the basic lines of the last—that
is, it is perpendicular to the axis of the shoe and makes a stand-

ard angle with a line from heel to toe. This gives a positioning factor somewhat like that in the engine line. Suitable "instructions" can tell the machine what size last it is working on and thus how it is to travel in stitching, nailing, and so on.

An analogy may be useful here. All baseball players would bat a 1000 average if the bat automatically hit every pitched ball squarely. But the human eye, which controls the way the bat swings, is a faulty mechanism, especially when making very rapid decisions. It often gives the batter's muscles the wrong information; he swings and connects poorly or not at all. You could probably build a batting machine that would turn in a 1000 performance, so long as you pitched balls within its reach. That is actually what the shoe-machinery people are aiming to do with shoes. Any shoe can be built precisely and uniformly if the information given the machine is accurate enough.

The intelligence plate not only positions the last, but carries other holes which form a code to tell the machine what size shoe to make and what routine to follow in doing it. Here is where electronics comes in. As soon as the last is oriented by the main heel "thimble," or hole, feelers in the machine seek out the remaining holes, whose positions can give a wealth of special information. Electronic circuits, instructed by the hole code, can readily translate the information into settings which bring every element of the shoe into position and do the correct work on it.

The code can also include instructions for making automatic gauging tests of each operation and by feedback correct any error that may be developing. If the work is within tolerances, the correcting function "makes no comment."

USMC has turned all this into actual hardware in the form of an automated shoe "rink" which carries out four of the main operations of building a shoe. The rink is presided over by one man, replacing the four usually needed to run the four components. He does not make shoes, but feeds in the materials,

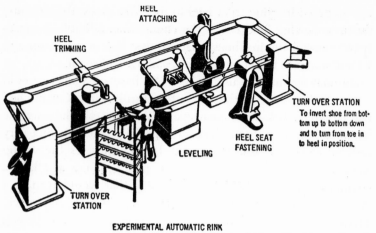

EXPERIMENTAL AUTOMATIC RINK

(*United Shoe Machinery Corp.*)

Automatic shoe rink

clears the finished product, and sees that everything stays in order. Part of the automation of this rink is that it transports the shoe from one station to the next without human intervention. In transit the shoe is positioned so as to be ready for the next operation. The thimble in the last makes it all possible.

At present, this rink is small and only does certain work at the heel end of the shoe. It is experimental only. If the shoes its turns out are as good as those done by hand, shoe automation is assured, for its speed and economy are far ahead of present methods. The inventors believe that an entire shoe line can be made automatic, with transfer tables interspersed between manufacturing stations all the way, and all under control of an electronic computer which takes its orders from the intelligence plate on the last.

There are many advantages ahead for the automated shoe factory. Speed is the first, for no time will be lost in exercising artistic judgment or in correcting mistakes. Nor will it take any appreciable time to position the lasts or to adjust them for irregularities. The old delays cause by hand transportation between machines will be gone; the shoe line will be virtually a continuous process, with all the savings and efficiencies of continuous flow.

A technical improvement of great importance to the trade will be the so-called two-part last. These forms are now carved out of one piece of wood; the geometric type has been designed with heel and toe made separately and hinged together. The purpose is to take advantage of an interesting mathematical relationship. The heel section of a certain size of shoe happens to be identical, in this system, with a similar section of a different size *in another width*. This means that a single heel size can be used to make a whole group of sizes, using different toes. In a typical tariff of 210 sizes, only 30 different heels are needed. This results in a very considerable economy in manufacturing lasts. The heels are interchangeable at the hinge.

It happens, too, that heel styles differ much less than toe styles. Hence the same heel will do duty on a number of styles, in the geometric system. As many as seven styles have been served by the same heel. Here we have another economy.

Again, there will be great advantages from accuracy. Since automatic machines can turn out products to much stricter tolerances, the old-fashioned job of matching up shoes to make nearly perfect pairs won't be needed. Accuracy as much as ten times greater than at present is expected. Meanwhile, the geometric system does away with errors in style in the extreme sizes—an esthetic improvement. It is also a very practical improvement. In orthopedic shoes, for instance, it is important to be able to rely on the exact performance of the shoe which the doctor prescribed. Old-style orthopedic shoes do not provide quite the same support on large feet as they do on small ones, because of the distortion in proportions of the arithmetic method of grading. Geometric-made shoes are all identical as to therapeutic action.

Another advantage, which is industry-wide, relates to labor. Present shoe workers are miserably underpaid, because slow hand work does not command high wages. Automatic machine operators are another matter. Their skills will not be of the hand but of the brain. Instead of being responsible for a machine costing the manufacturer, say, $5000, they will run one worth $40,000 to $50,000. A more complicated and costly machine takes a better trained and higher paid man to care for it.

Besides this, the new shoe worker will have a more demanding kind of responsibility because of the higher quality of his product. With tighter standards, it will be his job to get top performance out of his machine as well as out of himself. His responsibility to the customer—the wearer of the shoe—will be more direct. Indeed, he will be his own quality-control authority. Again, better pay for more exacting work.

Last, and by no means least, automatic shoemaking will mean a lower price for a pair of shoes. Even with cheap labor now, shoes are climbing into luxury brackets. This is dead wrong for basic commodities that are prime necessities for everyone. If the same labor force can make twice as many shoes in the same time, and if materials, such as synthetic leather and rubber can be lined up, shoe prices should turn sharply downward. Automation in shoes, as well as in everything else, will, in the end, benefit everyone.

11 | OIL ALMOST REFINES ITSELF

If you are in any doubt that automation has taken a powerful hold on America, you should take a trip through an oil refinery. Charter members of the automation family are the various chemical-processing industries. A pioneer among them is oil. The controls which make them work are essential to them and to our world-on-wheels. Eugene Ayres, a well-known engineer in this game, says this:

If the 50,000 control devices in the oil refineries of the U.S. should go "on strike," we would be faced with social disaster. The refineries would become lifeless industrial monuments. If we undertook to replace them with old-fashioned, manually-operated refineries to supply our present motor fuel needs, we would have to build four or five times as much plant, cracking and some other modern chemical processes would have to be eliminated, yields of motor fuel from crude petroleum would drop to a quarter of those at present, costs would skyrocket and quality would plummet. Automobile engines would have to be radically redesigned to function with inferior fuel. And because of lower motor-fuel yields, we would need to produce crude petroleum several times as rapidly as we produce it now. Technology in refining would be set back to the early 1920s.*

* Eugene Ayres, "An Automatic Chemical Plant," *Scientific American,* September, 1952. Mr. Ayres is a chemist with the Gulf Research and Development Company.

(*American Petroleum Institute*)

Silhouette of an oil refinery

This is a pretty strong statement. It says, in effect, that since 1920 we have built a brand-new kind of gasoline plant which *has* to be automatic to work, and we have redesigned our automotive economy to fit it. It points to the fact that automation began its work in chemical processing at least 35 years ago.

As you enter the gates of a modern refinery, you are surrounded by a world truly composed of mechanical giants. No science-fiction addict ever wandered in imagination through a stranger environment than that to be found in some 70 huge refineries dotted over the United States. Two characteristic features strike you at once: the miles of pipe and the forest of towers. These are obviously the essentials of the process. The oil travels hundreds of miles in its journey from crude to gasoline. To get there it must undergo innumerable delicately adjusted processes scattered over acres of ground. Most of these are done in tall, thin chambers that stand black against the sky, many towering a hundred feet or more into the air. A third thing to remark in this iron jungle is that there is nobody around. The plant very nearly runs itself.

The basis for the whole thing is that petroleum, as it comes out of the ground, is composed of a mixture of many hydro-carbons—that is, chemical compounds of hydrogen and carbon. The hydrocarbon family has a fascinating array of some hundreds of thousands of members, only a handful of which will form a vapor in air and burn. It happens that a generous share of that handful is found in petroleum. The game is to separate them out according to their composition to get various gasoline stocks, fuel and lubricating oils, tars, waxes and other chemicals. One of these is butane, from which synthetic rubber is made.

Today, the criterion in gasoline is the "octane rating"—a much-bandied phrase that is poorly understood by the public. You don't get high- or low-octane gasoline directly out of crude oil, but arrive at it by blending various gasoline stocks of different chemical composition. Technically, the rating of 100 on the scale is arbitrarily assigned to the hydrocarbon known as *iso-octane*, C_8H_{18}, while zero rating is given to a simpler compound called *heptane*. Both will vaporize and burn in an engine, the difference being in the amount of detonation or knock that they cause. A standardized test engine with a certain compression ratio will knock its head off with heptane but not with iso-octane. The latter burns "slowly," while the former explodes, more like TNT. The slower and more even the burning, the better the engine can utilize the fuel energy. Hence, iso-octane should be the ideal fuel. It is not, because of other factors such as high volatility. So, in practice, a number of different gasoline stocks of varying octane rating are blended to give an over-all rating of 90 or more. This works very well in today's medium-high-compression car engines.

The objective of the refinery, then, is to produce these various stocks and a large number of by-products, from the crude. Petroleum refining is nearly 100 years old. At first nothing was salvaged but kerosene. Simple stills were used that lost the high-volatile components and wound up with kerosene and heavy tars. As time went on, improvements began to uncover the lighter fractions; by the time gasoline engines were invented, there was a fairly satisfactory fuel for them. These early engines had such low compression ratios that even kerosene would not knock in them.

In order to catch the more volatile compounds, the still was abandoned in favor of the "fractionating tower." The principle of this is to heat crude oil until it is all in the form of vapor. The hot vapor is then introduced into the bottom of a tall cylinder and allowed to rise and cool through a series of interconnecting chambers, each with a bottom to it and a side outlet. As each petroleum fraction has a different boiling point, it will condense at a different temperature. Thus, the heavier fractions condense at the higher temperatures near the bottom of the tower, while the lighter ones continue upward as vapor, condensing near the top. The various outlet pipes from the tower therefore produce different grades of hydrocarbon: asphalts and coking oils at the bottom, working up through diesel and furnace oils to kerosene, and finally gasolines at the top.

This much had become a well-developed art in the 1920's. At this stage, refining was done entirely by the batch process. A charge of crude would be started through the system and followed through to its end products. Then another charge would be treated. However, the discovery of mass-production methods in Detroit shortly after the First World War was beginning to make the automobile a family institution, and the demand for gasoline rose steeply. Batch processing was expensive, slow and inefficient. Quality and yield were poor. So refinery engineers began a search for a continuous method of refining crude. A distilling line that never stopped would be faster, more efficient and produce better quality products. But it could not be run "by hand."

The secret of continuous refining lay in extremely reliable control. Temperatures and pressures must be maintained at precise values in every part of the system. Since refineries are outdoors and subject to weather changes, and since crude petroleum is not uniform in composition, non-stop refining meant continuous control at every instant. Human beings cannot do this very well. To handle a valve wheel as big as a tractor tire, while staring at a flowmeter dial for hours on end, is too much for human endurance or capabilities. It is also much too dangerous. Complete mechanization would be necessary before continuous processing could be realized.

In the period from 1920 to 1940, therefore, a gradual surrender of human muscle and judgment in favor of automatic operation took place. And with each step toward full mechanization, better yield from crude and better quality of the end products resulted.

During the 1930's, refining arrived at a peak of efficiency. There were only moderate improvements in prospect, it seemed: better instruments, more automatic controls, only a slight increase in yield to be expected. Then, suddenly, a wholly new principle appeared. Eugene Houdry, a chemical engineer, developed the catalytic-cracking process.

One of the more plentiful intermediates coming out of the fractionating tower is called "gas oil." Below kerosene in volatility (above it in boiling point), this product was taking a large bite out of a barrel of crude and sending it to relatively stagnant heavy-fuel markets. Houdry discovered that the hydrocarbon molecule in gas oil could be cut up or "cracked" into two or more light fractions if it was intensely heated and passed over a catalyst. This is a chemical compound that, for a yet unknown reason, can promote a chemical reaction between compounds mixed with it, but without itself taking part in the reaction. Like a golden key to a treasure chest, it can be used again and again without loss.

"Cat crackers" began to come in rapidly. In fact, a whole new branch of science called catalytic chemistry blossomed out.

It was responsible for synthetic rubber and for the vast field of synthesized chemicals which has given us plastics, new drugs, new paints, new industrial chemicals. Even now the field is barely opened. Cracked gasoline has been the leader from the first.

Not only did the cracking process give far more gallons of gasoline from a barrel of crude oil. Some of the gasolines were new, unobtainable by the older fractionating process. It was found that these new hydrocarbons made excellent blending agents, by which the octane ratings of commercial gasolines could be controlled with new precision. Actually, in the modern refinery, 44 gallons of gasoline can be recovered from 100 gallons of crude—several hundred per cent as much as 20 years ago.

Catalytic cracking compounded the need for automatic operation, for the handling of the elements is a critical process which no man can carry out by hand or by personal observation and judgment. And it also multiplied the danger. Temperatures of 800 or 900 degrees Fahrenheit, pressures of hundreds of pounds per square inch, flow rates of tons per minute—it must all be done by remote control. It was fortunate that the science of electronics, about this time, took a rapid jump ahead. No form of mechanical control is fast enough or delicate enough to maintain a continuous refining line in successful operation. So here we had a perfect field for automation.

One can get an idea of the furious pace and the brute force of modern refining by visiting a typical cat-cracking unit. You find yourself in a forest of weird monsters, seething with contained energy, roaring with the lifeblood that is coursing through them. The bowels of this giant are exposed to view. Thousands of snaking black pipes and tubes rise about you. As you stand on a broad concrete expanse, you are underneath it all. Great iron monsters soar on every side. It is incredible that any human brain could know enough to plan this intricate thing and make it work.

At the center of the lofty stage the two main actors seem to wade through their never-ending lines, arms entwined through a graceful run of huge pipe that loops down to the ground and up again between them. These are the Martians of the oil industry. The smaller—a huge cylindrical tank towering seventy feet—is the reactor, where gas oil is blown in with the catalyst, to be cracked on the run. The larger, of the same shape but twice as big around, is the regenerator, where the catalytic agent goes for a brief rest and cleaning.

The catalyst is a fine black powder. Tons of it circulate through the pair like blood through Siamese twins. In the infernal heat of the reactor, the powder picks up dirt and carbon and must continually be renovated. This is done simply by blowing vast quantities of air through it in the regenerator, igniting it, and burning away the contaminants. The catalyst itself does not burn.

The roar of the blowers makes talking impossible. These giants never stop, day or night, Sundays or holidays. They are shut down at most once a year, and then only for a thorough inspection and servicing that is crammed through at top speed. Only giants like these can keep up with the demand for gasoline. It is not barrels of it they produce in a day, but tons. A major refinery will turn out a quarter of a million barrels of products in one day. The "cat" and its regenerator will chew on 40 tons of catalyst every minute.

Here and there in the iron jungle you see a man. He may be hosing up a bit of the concrete base or feeling a valve or repacking a small pump. He is not contributing anything directly to the roaring mechanical circus going on above. He is neither needed nor tolerated in the process. A small square building nearby will show us why.

This is the control room. Inside, you find three sides completely occupied with instruments—perhaps sixty feet of them arrayed in banks and platoons and squads. There seem to be thousands. This is the place—the only place—to find out what is going on outside, for the entire process is mapped in every detail by a complex diagram of colored lines painted on the walls. The lines show the flow of the various fluids and are broken by circles and squares indicating valves and other controls. Associated closely with these indicated way-stations are the instruments that keep track of performance. Most of them are recorders of one kind or another. Compared to a man, they seem small and inactive. But they can do what he can't. Over wires and ganglia of small pressure tubes, they receive a continuous stream of messages from the crucial points of the line. Wherever temperatures may be critical or pressures essential, they know them. However a valve may be set, however fast a fan may be spinning or a pump stroke moving, they watch it instant by instant, and publish the news both by the indication of a hand on a dial and by a line drawn on a moving chart. If the sun goes in or a wind comes up they know of it the second it happens and record the change.

Mere statement of conditions, however, is only part of their job. Those temperatures and pressures and valve settings are all intimately interlocked. A variation at one point will affect everything along the line. Here comes automation again. Through electronic feedback, nothing important can be observed but some device compares the figure with required standards of performance and does something to bring it into line. There are no lone actors among this company of robots. A change at one point may require a score of changes elsewhere to compensate. Through computing mechanisms all the readjustments will be made together. And having been made through remote control, the new conditions will be investigated to see whether the right solution was found. In this maze of interconnected operations, all proceeding with vast power and

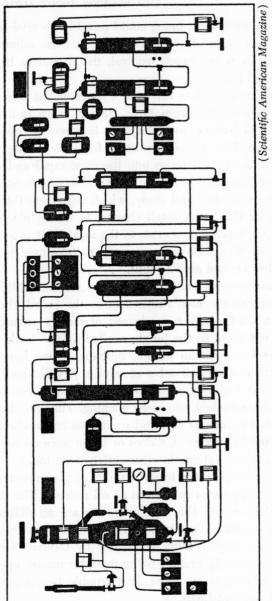

Oil refinery control board, from a photograph of the McMurrey Refining Co. near Tyler, Texas

(Scientific American Magazine)

infernal heat, no human being could possibly observe so complex an organization of variables, figure out the adjustments, and initiate, even by remote control, the delicately balanced changes called for.

There are men there, in the control room—half a dozen, perhaps—but they do not seem busy. Rather, there is a joking, relaxed kind of waiting going on. This is somewhat deceptive, for these men, like surgeons waiting for their patient to be anesthetized, are poised to go into the most rapid and skillful action if need arises. They have acquired a sixth sense, compounded of experience and study, which tells them things are going well, or that some small change, in taking place innocently enough, represents a crisis in the making. It is then that they stand by their instruments, ready to take over instantly if the smallest control activity fails.

A gong clatters out across the room, a red light blinks on. Leisurely, one of the men strolls over to the board, throws a switch, watches the effect on dozens of meters around him. Something out there in the jungle needed a little bucking up. It called for help. For an instant, perhaps, it was beyond its mental depth and needed a bit of advice. A valve had stuck; a lump of dirt had clogged a small pipe somewhere. Maybe a bird had been sucked into some opening. The "cat" had had an unexpected change of diet and wanted to know whether its digestion would be affected. Crises of importance do not often happen. There are automatic crisis-anticipators, too.

There is no better place to get an idea of the importance of men in automatic factories than in an oil refinery. The tiny instruments that control this vast operation are no different in principle from those that will superintend the making of a shoe, yet their responsibility is greater by thousands of per cent. Correspondingly greater is the need for master operators who know what it is all about, how trouble begins and how it can be stopped at birth.

The degree of automation, of course, varies with the refinery. As each new one is built, it picks up the latest things in control, and presently is superseded by others still more modern. On the whole, though, there is no other American industry which has so consistently and wholeheartedly kept up with advances in technology, willingly spending hundreds of millions of dollars in this tremendously costly automation. Everybody has reaped the benefits. According to Eugene Ayres, improved refinery efficiency has saved 100 million barrels of petroleum a year that would have been lost by the methods of 1930. Gasoline, in spite of the decay of the dollar's value, costs about the same per gallon as it did 35 years ago, except for the fancy taxes that have been hung on it. Meanwhile, refinery employment has steadily increased, wages have moved up sharply, and the men have jobs demanding far higher skills than ever before.

The end is not yet in sight, for real feedback automation of the refining process is yet to come. With intermediate steps now well controlled, engineers are looking forward to what they call "end-point" control—to quote Ayres again, "a master controller which will continually analyze the end products, compute what changes must be made in the process conditions and signal instructions back to appropriate points. Many types of industrial automation already do this. In refinery work it is exceedingly difficult, because there is no simple standard by which petroleum products can be measured. In the same way that shoe lasts must be standardized before automatic shoemaking can begin, so there must be a hard-and-fast criterion for gasolines.

Several well-known instruments, coming out of the laboratory recently, are helping to make a start. Chiefly, these are the infra-red spectroscope, the mass spectrograph and the X-ray photometer. Between them they are able to make a continuous analysis of the product as it flows through a pipe, *without in-*

terrupting its progress. Carbon monoxide and dioxide, olefines, sulfur dioxide, methane, the important hydrocarbons and tetra-ethyl lead concentrations, all show up in percentages on the charts. The mass spectrograph, which was used in gigantic form in the atomic-bomb project to separate uranium isotopes, can detect and indicate eight separate hydrocarbons at once, actually by determining the slightly different weights of their molecules. This is of paramount importance to end-point control, for it tells specifically the percentage proportions of the various products which the refinery is making. It is only a step to the control arrangement in which these indications can be picked up by electronic devices and applied by feedback to maintain the intermediate functions at just the right level to produce a uniformly excellent end result.

That will not be a short step. There are none in automation. It is so incredibly complicated now that there are not men enough in America sufficiently skilled to bring it to us overnight. Every inch of the way must be hacked out of nature's storehouse by main force.

12 | THE AUTOMATIC PRODUCTION LINE

The General Electric Company defines automation as "continuous automatic production." In its ultimate form this includes "making, inspecting, assembling, testing and packaging." It generally means the production of vast quantities of identical objects, usually small, and is the goal of the automatic control engineer for small and medium-sized business. From an automation standpoint these producers of large-quantity items, destined for the ultimate consumer or for heavy industry as components, offer the largest potential market.

Automation has already gone so far among them that it is impossible for us even to scratch the surface of the applications in use today. So we must take a few at random to indicate overall methods. It would be hard today to visit a plant mass-producing anything, that was not in some degree automated. You will find it in bakeries, in paint factories, in the making of boxes and cartons, in hosiery mills, in the manufacture of electric-light bulbs and bottles, from end to end in the hardware field, in radio, in television, in automobile bodies and the manufacture of freight-car components. Simply choose your favorite.

The one outstanding objective is to arrange a *progressive* line of production which starts from the raw materials stored in bins or stacked in warehouses, and ends with finished products, back in the warehouses, ready for delivery. Automation is becoming the goal of innumerable firms for two reasons: to keep up with public demand and to cut costs in order to meet the competition of firms already automated.

Fortunately, automatic controls need not be adopted all at once, but can be achieved by progressive stages, so long as a long-range plan is used. The General Electric chart reproduced here indicates the various steps that can be taken in an average shop. It shows the manual area, the mechanization area and the automation area. In the first, skilled workers manipulate hand tools and simple machines: in the second, machines do

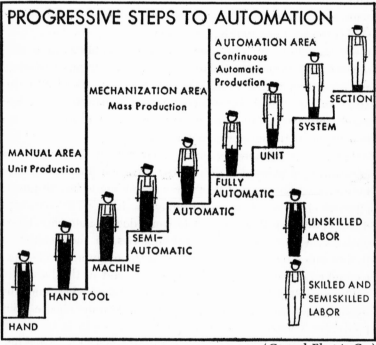

(*General Electric Co.*)

Progressive steps of factory automation

single specific operations under a more general human control. The automation area is divided into several stages. First we have fully automatic machines such as screw machines, which take metal in bar or rod form and turn out single pieces such as nails, screws, rivets and the like. These have been with us for a long time. Automatic machines of this sort make cartons and bottles in the same way. They do all the work on one piece of material.

In the second stage we have *groups* of automatic machines tied together by transfer tables. The result is an automated unit, which turns out some kind of a combination of single parts that naturally go together in permanent form. A wheel for a baby carriage, for example: spokes, spoke nuts, rim, hub, all made and put solidly together. The result is called a *component*. This is the stage we find in action today.

For the future we are aiming at *system* automation, a still longer line of automatic machines tied together to produce what is often called a *subassembly*. That would be the frame of the baby carriage, plus the wheels, brakes, tires, etc.; in other words, the chassis. All sorts of subassemblies will be made up by this method, often in different parts of the plant—metal bodies with fixtures in one place, upholstery in another. Each subassembly group is treated by its manufacturing area as if it were a complete product ready to ship. In fact, it is "shipped" from one area to another, complete with packaging if necessary, or stacked on "pallets" or in transporters of some other kind. Each finished subassembly constitutes the final responsibility of that automated line. It ends up with inspection, ticketing, accounting routines and warehousing.

The final target in these progressive steps is the automatic factory, where all operations necessary to turn out the finished goods are integrated. Subassemblies, still made in different areas, will be handled by a transportation system which is itself automated. Here, feedback control will be pushed to its utmost, for the machines themselves will have to check every step and signal back to earlier stages if anything goes amiss.

Two other stages can be added to the automatic factory to make it completely self-serving: materials-handling and classification at the beginning, and a tie-in with the office accounting and billing routines at the other end. Both are enormously important fields in their own right. Both involve data-processing "mechanical brains" which we will meet a little later on.

The paramount consideration in steadily increasing automation in the average plant is that it be kept *flexible*. We have seen how automatic control in automobile engine and steel plants is capable of manufacturing only one product. The equipment is hugely expensive, and if product design changes significantly, the machinery may have to be scrapped. Thus, automation engineers are constantly seeking to divide up a production line into as many small units as possible, consistent with efficiency. Then, if some product change comes along, only a part of the machinery may have to be altered or thrown out. They are also trying to design machines along the lines of the M.I.T. miller, with as much adaptability as possible.

Another matter of top importance is to so design the product that it can be made by automatic production. In the early days of automation, machines were built to duplicate human motions. Complications in the machines multiplied out of all proportion to the advantages of replacing humans. Then came a new technology called "product engineering." Spurred on by Diebold and others, designers began their thinking with, "How would we *like* to make this product?" instead of "How *must* we make it?" The result was the growing tendency to change the product itself in order to make it more efficiently. Sometimes a mere bump of metal added to a casting would allow an automatic machine to position it. The holes in the intelligence plate of a geometric shoe last do this sort of thing. Sometimes the whole product would need changing, or would be better done with some new material. Same end result, same utility, but altered so that an automatic process could turn it out at high speed. The kitchens of the nation are filled with gadgets that demonstrate this tendency.

The first automobiles looked like carriages; the modern car does not. A carriage was not adaptable to manufacture in automatic machinery; it was built. Diebold mentions the case of a stove company which turned out 16 styles of kitchen range. Embracing automation to cut costs, they adopted *one* basic design that could be trimmed to meet several price brackets. Result: prices in all brackets dropped.

Perhaps the best example of partial automation, embodying most of these principles, is in radio-set making. Literally millions of sets are turned out by scores of manufacturers in a keen competition which demands the shaving off of every penny of production cost. It used to be that hundreds of girls sat all day long at endless benches, picking little radio gadgets out of boxes, seizing a chassis panel from one box, whisking a maze of pre-cut wires from another, then painstakingly locating each element in the right spot, lining it up and soldering it deftly to the right-colored wires. It took a girl quite a while to learn the pattern of all this. During training she cost her company a good deal in mistakes; later, she cost them more in absences and quittings-to-get-married.

In the midst of World War II, John Sargrove, an English radio manufacturer, broke this jam and started radio assembly toward automation. He did it by *rethinking* his product. He figured that the worst bottleneck was in the wiring of the panels. Was there any reason why a panel must have wires? Conductors, yes, to connect the right terminals. But not necessarily wires. What better way might there be to achieve that rat's nest of connections than separate wires, each with its color code? The answer was pretty obvious. Why not plate the back of the panel with thin copper, then remove most of it, leaving narrow copper tracks going to the right places?

Sargrove's brilliant idea required skillful redesign of the panel layout, relocating some of the components on the front of the board so that channels wouldn't cross and short-circuit. But these details were quickly attended to. A method was found for coating the copper with a "ground" or wax, along the paths desired for the circuit, then etching away the remaining exposed copper, removing the ground, and ending up with an electrical "map" of the circuit.

Today, even the most intricate circuits can be "printed" through a steel stencil plate, using a special "ink" resistant to etching acid. After the spare copper has been dissolved away, the ink can be dissolved off, leaving neat, bright copper paths. It can all be done by a single machine. Printed circuits are now virtually standard in radio and in many other types of electronic equipment. The jungle of wiring inside a TV set has not yet succumbed, but it will. More than one television repairman has told me ruefully that he dreads that day. He is used to the chaos of little colored wires and fears he will get lost if things are too neat. The manufacturer is not impressed. *He*

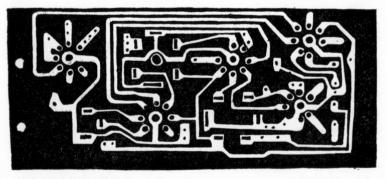

A printed circuit

thinks of the extra thousands of sets he could sell for less if he could automate his production lines.

A further step in the automation of making radios is in the development laboratory, and about to emerge. Instead of having lines of girls endlessly fitting components into printed panels with flying fingers, choosing by habit and feel the right condenser or resistor, the right end up, and putting each of their terminals through the right hole, a machine will do it. The United Shoe Machinery Corporation has worked out a radio-assembly line and so have General Electric and many other pioneers. Dr. Joseph Harrington, Jr., was the principal brain behind the United Shoe program, which we may take as a typical example.

Harrington began his thinking at the soldering point on the panels. Why did the girls have to touch each terminal with a soldering iron? Would a machine do it better? His first experiment was to have the girls assemble the components into the right panel holes, then dunk the panels bodily in a vat of molten solder, fastening all connections at once. It worked well, but was still wasteful of time. A girl had to fish a resistor, say, out of a box, bend its terminals properly, insert the piece into its correct place and go on to another. Still too much hand work and an intelligence level too low for human beings.

The next idea was to construct a machine that would insert the parts all at once. Two solutions were possible: first, to make the machine do what the girls did—pick parts out of boxes, "feel" them into place, then bend over their wires. Second, to redesign the parts themselves so that the machine could handle them in a way natural to machines. Harrington adopted the second. To do so he had to cause a minor revolution among the makers of standard radio components such as condensers, grid leaks, and resistors. All of these are pretty much alike, small cartridges about the size and shape of a lipstick. Harrington's laboratory developed a machine which would take these cartridges and line them up, "bumper to bumper," then stick them to bands of masking tape to form a long belt. The belt could now be fed through an assembly machine like bullets through a machine gun—at high speed.

His next venture was the assembling machine itself. As it has worked out, it is a multiple-station affair on the pattern of a model railroad. The radio panels travel along the rails, securely fixed to pallets. As each comes into a station it stops, signaling its presence to the "stationmaster," an electronic control. The proper baggage is then loaded on; that is to say, a component is picked up from a particular reel of the right kind of part by a mechanized arm, pushed down into the right holes and its nubs of wire bent flat on the under side, ready for soldering. As the whole row of panels travels like a train, at one speed, each panel reaches a station at the same time and all get loaded simultaneously. The next instant the train moves on to the next loading point.

Harrington added a typical automated gadget at each station, by inserting a checking device to see if the right component was being installed. This is merely an electrical "bridge," to test the values of resistors and condensers. The trick does away with the mistakes even the most experienced girl will make by snatching a component from the wrong box. A machine-assembled panel *has* to work.

Another advantage of assembly automation is that it is as flexible as a toy railroad would be. The kind of component loaded at any station can quickly be changed. Stations can be added or omitted. By replacing loading heads, quite different assemblies, using new circuits, can be turned out on the same line. A skilled attendant can change a head in three minutes.

There are two routes of progress in assembly-line automation. Some believe that the whole line should be contained in one machine. The parts disappear into it, the product comes out. Others prefer the "open" line, with component devices that can be replaced individually. For many products, especially those for the military, this seems the wiser course. The Air Force, for instance, required a few radar reflectors made in a hurry for the Distant Early Warning network in northern Canada. They were made by hand methods at high expense and considerable loss of time. They could have been made on a machine like Harrington's or on one similar to M.I.T.'s milling machine, in far shorter time and at lower cost.

On test runs Harrington's radio line has turned out typical radio-panel assemblies at the rate of one every five seconds, 720 an hour, better than 11,000 in a two-shift working day. On a 250-day yearly schedule it could produce millions, and they needn't all be identical. If improvements came along, they could easily be incorporated during brief shutdowns, or during the empty third shift.

One twist in the automation of repeated operations is reliability. Errors committed by the machinery work against you in a geometric ratio. A Yale lock of 50 parts, say, will chalk up a near-perfect score if the machine's various processes all work with a 99.999 per cent average of no mistakes. But if the average reliability of each machine component is only 95 per cent perfect, then you're in trouble. Your final product stands only a 13 per cent chance of having no defects in it. Thus, if a single complicated machine does all the operations, it must be virtually foolproof. The open-line type of automation poses no such problem, since individual components can be watched and serviced to keep them in 100 per cent perfect trim.

It would be a hopeless task, even in these early days of automation, to cover the entire field of applications. Most of them are reasonably similar to radio. A few general considerations cover them all. A booklet setting forth the many ways that automation can be used to speed up production and improve quality, reads like a fairy story.

The first thing you note in the newly automated plant is tidiness. Machines are neater and more compact. Floor space is much less. In one well-known case the newly automated line takes 16 square feet of space, as against 800 for the old method. Then you note that there are many methods coming under the heading of automatic production. In one General Electric system a skilled machinist makes a pilot run through a job while his every motion is recorded on magnetic tape. Thereafter, the machine will make identical parts from the tape, without the machinist. Another machine uses templates or models, like a last-lathe.

Automation of the inspecting routines are common nowadays. Once the significant dimensions, weights, etc., have been determined and programmed into the inspecting devices, the parts can go through them in an unending procession, and no error will be missed.

Assembling can be done automatically if the product is not too large or complicated. As James R. Bright points out, anything *can* be assembled by machines.* But in some industries, assembly is the principal cost factor and it would be fantastically expensive to automate. It is theoretically possible to put a big airplane together this way, using Martian giants costing billions. But who would do it? So automated assembly belongs to products that are made in vast quantity and all alike.

Finally, automation can and does do a vast array of packaging jobs. It is remarkable how large an object can be machine-packed. Refrigerators are one example. In this case the carton is built around the product. Huge sheets of corrugated cardboard are laid flat and reinforced with wood, then folded up around the box by machine. The robot closes, staples and marks the box, too.

Packaging and materials-handling are a separate phase of automation that is not new. As we go on, from time to time we

* J. R. Bright, "How to Evaluate Automation," *Harvard Business Review,* July-August, 1955.

shall see automatic packaging being done in a variety of ways. We shall see, also, how materials-handling techniques have come under the automator's eye in ways that are as different as the products. The parts that go into General Electric refrigerators, for example, are not warehoused and fetched to the assembly points by hand. Instead, they are carried around the assembly building on an overhead railroad. As a particular part reaches the point where it is to be used, it automatically drops off into place. If it is too soon, and others are ahead of it, it waits on a siding. And if the siding is loaded to capacity, the part simply stays on the main line and makes another circuit of the building. It takes ten miles of track and 150 miles of control wires to run this automaton, but it saves enormously in man-hours, and assembly machines are never held up for parts.

13 | BEER AND PRETZELS

"You can't make peanut butter in an oil refinery," is a crack that automation experts are fond of making. Nor can you make beer on a radio-assembly line, alas. Each industry has its own peculiar problems in automatic control. The product dictates the method. Often times you can redesign the product to suit the principles of mechanization and come out with a better product than you had before. Not with beer. In the case of soft drinks, the whole process of mixing and packaging can be carried out in one large machine. Almost every city has its cola plant. Syrup, water, and carbon dioxide, automatically mixed in the right proportions, and you have it. But not with beer.

I had heard that the new Anheuser-Busch brewery in Los Angeles was turning out Budweiser by the most modern methods, with a generous share of automation involved, and went to see them. The result of this visit, therefore, is a report on the latest and presumably the fastest and best way to brew beer.

Beer making is certainly a mass-production industry. The brewery in question turns out close to a million barrels a year. It is not, however, a continuous process, nor is automation likely to make it one. For centuries beer has been made in batches, in kettles and tanks. It is still made that way, in larger kettles and tanks. Automation experts do not favor the batch method, but seek to make every process conform to the continuous-flow scheme. Beer making, being as much of an art as it is a science, does not lend itself to the continuous method. The automation experts have had to do the best they could on that basis.

One of the first questions I asked my engineer-guide was whether it would be possible to turn beer making into a continuous-flow process. He shook his head vigorously. "The next step," he said, "would be to invent a machine that would drink the beer." At first thought this seemed like the hard core of tradition, resisting change. But you have here, in reality, a much broader question. The brewing of beer is an art. Should an art be automated, for the sake of reaching everybody with a low-cost product? It is one of the considerations we have to deal with in this pioneering stage of the new industrial economy. For my money, beer and the other arts should be left alone.

People have the same feeling about beer that they have about the Brooklyn Dodgers—an intensely personal tie with the art. They like to know that they are drinking something that has been built by hand, lovingly. The brewer's problem is to produce his brew in massive quantities without losing the personal touch. In a brewery there is one man only who can fulfil that office. He is the brewmaster. This shadowy character, seldom seen, is a king, superior in his field to vice-presidents and the chairman of the board. For it is a million barrels of his delicate judgment that they sell.

The brewmaster tastes every batch before it goes on to the bottling works. Along the way he stares repeatedly at streams of wort, judging color, clarity, specific gravity. Farther back, he and his men study the grains, the hops, the water. They pore over temperature charts and elapsed time. They hunt for the ultimate speck of dust and scrutinize the linings of the tanks and kettles for the merest blemish. How can you automate a job like this? You may rig up an automatic temperature control to a fraction of a degree at every point, as they do in oil, but you can't mechanize the subtle variables that result in the quality of a beer, because that quality can't be defined.

Thus, we have here, by way of contrast, a case where automation has got to adapt itself to conditions that are foreign to it. Brewing is still largely a matter of human judgment, raised to a gigantic production scale. It is significant that in spite of the poor climate for it, automation helps beer quite a lot.

The process begins with grain—rice and the malt from barley. The two are mixed with water separately and then combined and strained. The liquid that comes off is called "wort," and is the beer stock. This wort is now boiled vigorously in huge kettles, while hop blossoms are thrown in, to give the delicate flavor and pleasing aroma. The wort is strained again, cooled, and transferred to fermenting tanks, where yeast is added. Fermenting takes from one to two weeks, after which the brew, now beer, is ready for a thorough settling, filtering and the generating of carbon dioxide. It is finally set aside in refrigerated tanks for prolonged ageing, and is then ready for bottling and canning.

From the outside, the brewery is a cluster of tall, windowless buildings that might be warehouses. But inside it is a wonderland of neatness and white tile. Tile floors, tile walls, gleaming stainless steel kettles as big as small houses; a few pipes; still fewer men. Those one does see are eternally scrubbing floors that have just been scrubbed.

From start to finish, precision is the word. Automation meets you at once. The grain silos, in their own separate building, are attended by nobody. Across the alley, high up in the brew house, there is a small control panel. As the batching begins, an assistant brewmaster goes to it briefly and sets up the routine for raw-materials flow. A diagram of colored lines on the board tells him of the various routes that can be followed from storage to the weighing machines at the top of the brew house. He chooses the grain bins he wants to draw from, and the conveyor routes he prefers, and turns various knobs which set switching mechanisms along the way. Red lights blink on if certain conveyors are in use, and he makes a second choice. A touch on a master button starts the delivery. The grain is brought directly to the weighing machines automatically.

The weighing itself, however, is a manual operation, carried out by a brewmaster's assistant. There are two scales, one for each grain, and the operator watches the scale dials until the

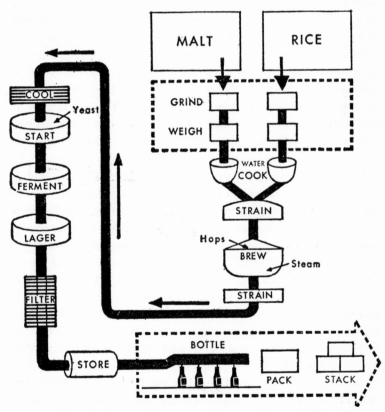

Beer production line with automated areas shown in dotted boxes

quantity ordered by the brewmaster has been reached, then shuts off the flow. Rice and malt are then dumped into separate grinding machines, where they are reduced to a fairly fine powder. Moving downward by gravity, the ground materials arrive in tanks, where a carefully measured volume of water is added to each. The two then enter a header which delivers them to a combining tank. They are now called the "mash."

Art has now taken over, although science is not far behind. The first objective is to obtain a solution of certain definite factors in the grains, which will contain the sugars necessary for fermentation. Both rice and malt contain starch, but starch will not ferment; it must first be converted into sugar. The malt, however, possesses certain enzymes which are able to carry out this conversion. Now the mash is heated, to promote the reaction. The time and temperature of this operation are critical, and the brewmaster watches them with close attention. This is not a whim on his part; he is simply exercising a keen knowledge of biological chemistry. An error in either factor will damage the tiny enzymes or fail to complete the reaction.

Next in line comes a tremendous straining tank, into which the combined malt and rice mash is discharged. Here, a perforated false bottom screens out the malt hulls, which settle to form a filter bed. Quiet agitation with a big surface sweep keeps the liquid moving just enough to prevent the filter layer from packing too tight. From this bed flows a clear sweet liquid called "wort," which is now ready for brewing. Down through the floor through a pipe as big as a small storm drain comes the wort, some 650 barrels of it, and the giant brew kettle below is filled.

Here is the most spectacular part of the equipment. The kettle, perhaps 20 feet in diameter, sits deep in the floor, a gleaming mass of polished stainless steel. It is completely enclosed by a conical dome which has a small door in it. Most of the units from here on have doors like this, and you can see the brew through them from time to time as it travels from kettles to vats to tanks. It is through the first of these doors that the brewmaster's loving care and the hop flowers go in. The brew kettle is heated by a gigantic percolator coil carrying live steam, which soon makes the charge of wort boil violently. It takes vigorous action to extract the essential hop oil from the little plant that makes beer taste like beer.

From here on we have the ancient German process of beer making, in all essentials the same as it has been for centuries. The only modern contributions are increased size and the clusters of recording instruments which extend the brewmaster's critical senses to the insides of the containers. At each step, scientific sampling is done. There is a laboratory where technical tests are made on each batch. But there is no real automation. Nothing is fed back, except what goes down human throats.

Mechanical handling, of course, comes into it. Most of the equipment is in duplicate or triplicate, so that one group can be cleaned and serviced while another is making beer. The many pumps and valves offer something of a problem. No machinery runs without oil, yet the brewmaster will not allow even a drop of it to get into his precious brew. Extraordinary care is taken to protect the wort as it flows. Even the air compressors, used in many parts of the system, have piston rings of pure carbon, that do not need lubrication. The pumps get along on beer.

Many stages of the process must be handled at low temperature—the fermenting, for instance. The brewery has a powerful refrigerating plant, largely automatic, supplying whole areas with unrelenting cold. Hops are stored near the freezing point; the beer, once made, never rises above 50 degrees until it comes out into the bottling works.

Unique with Budweiser, carbon dioxide is generated by the beer itself, rather than by introducing bottled gas. Before final filtering, a huge "lager tank" is charged with a layer of sterilized beechwood chips, to help clarify the beer during its long ageing period. Then the tank is partly filled with finished beer. A carefully measured portion of partially fermented brew is added. With this mixture a slow second fermentation takes place, which enlivens the beer with its own natural carbonation, CO_2 being a by-product of fermentation.

Beer making today would fall far behind if top speed were not used in bottling and canning. This is all science and no art. The brewmaster is not concerned. Packaging by machine is one of the oldest forms of automation. With beer the method is much like that used in packing candy, cigarettes or milk. An endless line of bottles or cans comes in at one end of a huge room on a conveyor. Unit after unit is seized by mechanical hands, filled, sealed, labeled, packed and shot out in cartons at the other end for warehousing.

You see the file of bottles clinking along on a narrow belt single-file, marching toward a big circular machine that is all any engineer could desire in the way of complication. Into its maw the bottles disappear, only to march out again, filled. Beer has been piped over from the storage tanks underground. The capping operation follows the filling immediately, in a noisy robot that never stops its *grump-um-grump-um-grump* from one end of a work-shift to the other.

There is a merry ring to the bottles as they jockey one another along to the pasteurizing apparatus. They might be chattering for joy.

Labeling follows, then an innovation that is important: a test for contaminants in the beer, worked out by Radio Corporation of America. Little foreign matter could have got into the beer, with all this care, you would say. But with the tremendous speed of bottling it is still conceivable that a tiny flake of glass or bit of dirt might have been sealed in. A bottle of beer with anything in it but beer is not in the cards. The machine that detects contamination and eliminates the unacceptable bottles is the last word in automatic quality control.

Fairly small and cylindrical in shape, this gadget's heart is a photo-electric tube. A beam of light shines on it after passing through each bottle. The tube "recognizes" the nature of shadows that are caused by irregularities in the bottle glass or by foreign matter, and takes appropriate electronic action. As the endless line of filled bottles parades around inside the machine, they are given a rapid whirl by small rotating holders. This spins the liquid and so carries around any loose solid material. As each bottle reaches the light beam it is suddenly arrested in its turning. But the liquid goes on spinning. Thus, imperfections in the glass walls appear to the photo-tube as isolated spots, while floating matter looks like streaks. If a streak is detected, the machine's "memory" earmarks that bottle for the scrap heap as it leaves the machine. Stationary spots are ignored.

Carton loading is a routine job done by a mechanical packer which seizes a caseful of bottles by their necks and plunks them down into waiting boxes every second or so. There is one further wrinkle, however, that gives automation a free hand here. Warehousing thousands of cartons of heavy bottles and cans is difficult, because when they are stacked in tiers a dozen or more high they can easily fall over. A special stacking machine solves this trouble by building the cartons into the form of a brick wall, with all joints between cartons overlapped or broken. Here is a machine that really "thinks," in its small way. Its job is to pile up layers of cartons on a movable pallet so that no two layers have the same conformation. It can do this because the cartons are oblong, not square.

The cartons slide into it from the top by way of a roller conveyor. As each carton arrives at a chute, it brushes past three switch arms, one after another. These send coded messages down to a small electronic computer beside the machine. The computer looks up in its memory to see what patterns of stacking it has used in previous layers, and sends back word that it is preparing such and such a pattern this time, which calls for this particular carton to go in long-way first. Metal arms seize the carton and carry out these orders as it is skidded down onto the pallet. Now the next carton arrives and is fitted into the chosen pattern in a similar way. When the layer of cartons is complete, the pallet is automatically lowered one tier, a metal sheet covers the cartons on it, and a new pattern of containers is slid on. The metal withdraws, returns on top, and the process is repeated. This goes on until a stack six or more high has been built onto the pallet. The whole works is finally shoved out on rails to await the man with the skip-loader, who picks up the block of interlocked cartons and deposits it on the warehouse floor. He doesn't even have to check to see that the cartons are all in order. This particular automated gadget is called the Lamson Pallet Loader and is a popular answer to many warehousing problems besides the stacking of beer.

No visit to a brewery will be complete without an invitation to the rathskeller, where you get as many foaming glasses of the brew as you can hold. Beer and pretzels, nothing else. But enough.

Pretzels are not, it turns out, made in a brewery. That is a specialty, you are assured, and one which disdains automatic manufacture. Talented girls, it seems, "tie" these strange little objects by hand, so lightning swift that no machine can duplicate their work.

This is not quite true. Like most other mass-produced items, pretzels have come under the gaze of the automation engineers. The experts wanted to cast them like cookies, for how would an eater know whether his pretzels are tied or not? The trade, however, wouldn't stand for it. So the American Machine and Foundry Company tackled the problem the hard way, intent upon copying exactly the motions the girls make in the tying operation. The result is an automatic pretzel-bender even more talented than the girls. One machine alone, it is averred, can tie 450,000 pretzels a day. A line of half a dozen of them could probably supply the beer drinkers of the entire continent.

Automation is on insecure ground here, though. Who knows what beer drinkers might do if they found out that the fingers that made their pretzels did not wear rings or flutter prettily through blond hair during the coffee breaks?

14 | FOR THE WORKER—
FAMINE OR PLENTY?

With this brief sketch of industrial automation, we can go on into the liveliest of all of automation's proving grounds—the office. Before doing so, however, it is important to consider just what is happening, and what may be expected to happen, to the industrial worker. His present job is being taken over by machines. What is he going to do? Will he be thrown out of work? Take an inferior job somewhere else? Train himself in time to reap the benefits of the new, up-graded jobs in automation?

It is a ticklish business to predict what will happen in so important a matter affecting so many people. I would much rather stick to simple facts. Unhappily, the facts of employment in industry in the next twenty years are not here, except as estimates and guesses. Most of these are colored by whatever pet convictions the guesser happens to have.

For example, Professor Norbert Wiener, in his book *The Human Use of Human Beings,* says, "Let us remember that the automatic machine . . . is the precise economic equivalent of slave labor. Any [human] labor which competes with slave labor must accept the economic conditions of slave labor. . . . This will produce an unemployment situation, in comparison with which the depression of the thirties will seem like a pleasant joke."

Edmund C. Berkeley, a long-time student of automation, thinks that "it is not only that life itself seems more greatly endangered than ever by the possible use of robot weapons in warfare. It is also that people are endangered economically— in their jobs and pocketbooks. The application of robot machines in industry plainly increases the hazards of unemployment." [*]

The United Automobile Workers of America, meeting some time ago at Atlantic City, passed a resolution on automation which included this:

Automation . . . and a host of other new developments hold tremendous possibilities for good or evil. Properly used, they can advance by many years the realization in America of man's age-old dream of an economy of abundance. Improperly used, for narrow and selfish purposes, they can create a social and economic nightmare in which men walk idle and hungry—made obsolete as producers because the mechanical monsters around them cannot replace them as consumers.

When CIO President Walter Reuther visited the famous Ford engine line in Cleveland, a company official indicated one of the automatic machines and chirped, "How are you going to collect union dues from these guys?" Instantly Reuther cracked back, "How are you going to get them to buy Fords?"

Everywhere that you look into accounts of automation advances, you read of the fear of workers being displaced. The Commonwealth Edison Company in Chicago is said to be using an IBM computing machine that will replace 200 people. An oil-industry expert has claimed that a refinery that employs 800 without automation could keep up the same production with 12 men under complete automatic operation. In the Ford plant,

[*] E. C. Berkeley, "2150 A.D.—Preview of the Robot Age," *New York Times Magazine,* November 19, 1950.

during the now-obsolete manual-production days, it required 400 men to turn out one finished engine block in 40 minutes. Now, 48 workers produce one every 18 minutes. Elsewhere, a huge transfer machine does 540 operations under the guidance of one man; the older method involved 35 to 75 men for the same rate of output. It is reported that in Boston in 1949, when long-distance telephone calls became automatic, 450 toll operators were given their termination notices. The list grows every day. Already it is well-nigh endless. If all this is true, is automation leading us to disaster?

Now on the other side there are just as many statistics and guesses. John Diebold says, categorically, "There will be no workerless factories as a result of automation. There will be no mass unemployment; contractions in one function will tend to be offset by expansions in other functions." President Paul B. Wishart of the Minneapolis-Honeywell Regulator Company says, "We have been told that machines replace men. Yet, by and large, every industry that has increased its investment per employee [by increasing automatic control] has increased its employment."

President Ralph J. Cordiner of General Electric told a Congressional subcommittee lately that, "Technological change is a gradual, evolutionary process which creates employment and exerts a stimulating and stabilizing effect on the economy. This can and will continue as long as business has the incentives and freedom to grow, and to create new products and industries."

As to new industries, many executives agree that automation will create a far wider demand for labor than it destroys. Dozens of America's largest corporations report that from a quarter to a half of their sales today are of products which did not even exist in their laboratories as ideas before World War II.

"Automation," says Dean E. Wooldridge of the Ramo-Wooldridge Corporation, "will become one of the largest—possibly even the largest—national industry." That would make it pretty large, and it would employ a lot of people. It seems to be a fact that, while automatic machines displace *direct* labor, they create more jobs than they destroy because they open up wholly new opportunities for a broader life and spark thousands of new demands. It looks as if those who view technological unemployment as an unavoidable curse of scientific progress are looking backward, not ahead. It looks as if the jobless thousands that automation is supposed to create will be those who cannot learn the new techniques fast enough. Nobody denies that these techniques result in better jobs, if a worker can be equal to their challenge.

Ted F. Silvey, who evangelizes steadily for the CIO on the dangers of automation, sardonically quotes a shop manager who is supposed to have said, "The only trouble with a factory is the people." He is not quite right. There is much trouble from the machinery, too. But it is undeniable that the people constitute the greatest problem *during a fundamental change.* The machines keep up with the brains of their inventors, but the workers may not have the benefit of such vigorous and enlightened thought.

The crux of the situation is, of course, education for the new day. Can it keep up? History is full of examples which show that it never keeps up, and that some are hurt. But history never shows that a reactionary attitude is useful, or that it ever survives. When James Hargreaves produced the first workable spinning machine in England in 1767, the old-time hand spinners tried to wreck his factory. In the next hundred years England became the foremost textile nation of the world; wages for textile workers went up 300 per cent and their numbers multiplied extraordinarily. The invention of the dynamo opened a new economic era, which no worker today would go without. Edison's light was an immediate consequence. The New Bedford whalers were wiped out, for whale oil was no longer needed for lamps. The gashouse workers, however, remained and multiplied, taking their places alongside the new millions of electrical workers in the service of home cooking.

A similar shift took place with the automobile. Not only were thousands of new jobs built upon the graveyard of the carriage maker and the coachman. Ramifications established the oil industry, gave enormous impetus to steel and chemicals, and created, almost overnight, the gigantic rubber industry. Tens of thousands found employment in road building, in manning gas stations and garages, in opening motels and taverns, in developing resorts. The automobile has been felt in many branches of the sporting-goods field, in clothing, cameras, picnic-basket making. Complete the list yourself. One would never have imagined all this while listening to the disgruntled hack driver and his dark forebodings.

The telephone industry, charter member of the automation family, has steadily eliminated hand jobs, and just as steadily employed new thousands. In steel, before automation in 1923, 420,000 men were at work in the United States. In 1952, with only partial automatic control, the figure had risen to 651,700. And this increase had its counterpart in the iron mines, on the lake boats, and in the countless array of new industries based on cheap steel. When Charles Hall discovered a way to produce pure aluminum inexpensively, his friends laughed at him. He and his sister were the only two employes in the industry in 1888. Would any reader care to compute the number of people directly and indirectly earning a living in aluminum today? It was cast iron and sheet iron that suffered from the "theft of markets" by the new aluminum pots and pans. Can anyone find the scars of unemployment on the ferrous metals industry now?

The real danger of unemployment, it seems, springs from the act of *holding back* when new things demand a hearing.

Only 30 people are needed to operate each of the isotope separation plants of the Atomic Energy Commission at Oak

Ridge, and most of these are untrained girls. But it takes more than 400 men of high skill to keep the apparatus running smoothly and safely. Hundreds of thousands of men and women are working in atomic energy now, with employment rocketing as each new milestone of progress is passed. Ten years ago most atomic engineers believed they would never live to see a significant use of the peaceful atom. The atomic art, indeed, was born automated. Human beings alone could not operate the processes a day without courting certain death.

Diebold explains why the maintenance of automatic machines can soak up direct unemployment. "Maintenance personnel in a fully automatic plant, with the most extreme policy of parts replacement, would still be very numerous. And it should also be borne in mind that the replaced parts must frequently be returned to the manufacturer for disassembly and repair, thus requiring much human labor at another location."

Mr. Cordiner, before the Congressional subcommittee, capsuled the matter quickly, into four new leads: Technological progress will create new employment (1) because of a sort of chain reaction of economic growth, (2) because service industries provide new jobs, (3) because the industries supplying automation and technological advance also create new employment opportunities, and (4) because entire new industries, employing thousands, are created by the new automation technologies. He added a point little appreciated outside factory management—normal factory turnover. This refers to the steady average of people who quit, retire, die, or change jobs. During 1954-55, 40,000 new employes were hired by General Electric to replace those who dropped out. In the same period at least 33,000 people shifted jobs within the company through promotions, technological improvements, and fluctuations in the forces needed in each operation. "We try to plan any substantial technological changes in such a way," said Cordiner, "that normal attrition will absorb the shift in employment. . . . When you couple these factors with the simple fact that the nation's appetite for goods in the next decade will rise faster than the number of people available to produce them, you can see why we feel that automation and technological progress are necessary and beneficial, and that they exert a stimulating and stabilizing effect on the economy."

The gist of what the automation experts in America say is that we are coming upon a vast time of plenty, *provided* that we accept automatic operation fast enough. The gist of what the union leaders say is that there is grave danger of serious dislocation. Thousands, perhaps millions, will be thrown out of work unless militant efforts are made to hold down the coming of automation. Who is right?

"Automation will mushroom," insists Dr. Gordon S. Brown, of the Massachusetts Institute of Technology, one of the key men in automatic-control techniques. "We want it to mushroom. We couldn't stop it even if we wanted to. It will bring great change to all of us."

"In the course of reaching higher standards of living," retorts the CIO, "we will not take one step backward in order to take two steps forward."

Thus, powerful forces of labor, capital, and science are lined up two against one in the automatic arena, with the workers in the middle. What is the workman to do? Is he to take the frightened view, the truculent view, or is he to take the openminded, progressive one? Purely for his own sake, if the patterns of past civilization have any meaning, he must take the latter.

I think what we most need at this stage is a note of hope. Everything in the past indicates that the world is going ahead. It also indicates that no progress is possible without pain and struggle and at least some jeopardy. An average man who believes his present employment is jeopardized by machinery would do better to study the situation and see how he can fit into changing times, rather than to stand where he is, threatening to stop the system altogether if it does not serve *him*. The workers of Belgium, who once threw their wooden shoes into the looms and thus became the original *saboteurs*, accomplished nothing but the loss of their shoes and their jobs. When Edison's office boy got fresh and the inventor fired him, the whole shop went on strike in sympathy with the child. When they came back they found that Edison had invented a machine to do the work they had been doing. They didn't work there any more. "They went out," Edison observed long after, "and they are still out."

Whether we like it or not, a machine is a dangerous thing to fool with.

There is a grim side to this. A man who has spent his life learning how to get along with one machine, suddenly finds that it can do without him. He falls easily into panic. He had thought that his job would go on forever; he had been told by his union that he and they are strong enough to *demand* that it go on forever. But now the new machine has come and he doesn't know where he stands. The orderly flow of his life is threatened. His security is toppling. He finds that he has got to protect himself somehow. But how?

This man has two courses open to him. Like King Canute, he can close his mind to the changing world he lives in. He can try to get from his leaders that measure of protection for which he has paid heavily in dues. Or, he can decide that his destiny is his own, as hundreds of millions less favored have to do every day. He can open his mind to the meaning and promise of automation and resolve to find his part in it, *not as a mob but as a man*. If he is smart, he will see that Dr. Brown is right —"we couldn't stop it even if we wanted to"—and he will look around for opportunities and methods of up-grading his skills, early in the game rather than late.

Countless citizens have taken this attitude throughout the

rise of America. They have not waited to be taken care of, but have faced the risks and uncertainties of change and have exploited their own imagination and vigor while the change was young. You can see this in the radio and television industries; virtually every industrial leader in America saw it at some time in his youth. The matter really boils down to this: If you want the security of a job that will never change, you will have to take a job so poor that it cannot change. If you want a better job than that, you will have to accept the hidden risk of its disappearing and being replaced by something better. This is no hazard induced by the much maligned profit system. It is a hazard of life itself, like the hazards to health, to love, to comfort, to the very continuance of existence. It may be trite to say that there is no easy road, but in dealing with automation it is well to remember that the whole weight of civilization is on the side of progress. To stick with a system that is on the wane is folly.

What can the unions do about automation? Again, they have two courses: to bristle and plant their feet and make big talk about what they will and will not permit (imagine what happens to a scientist who tries to do that with a stream of electrons!). Or, they can take the vigorous attitude that belongs with the scientists. Here is a new thing that will mean enormous benefits to all people. Anything we can do to bring about an orderly advance into it, we will do. It is bound to help us, too. Many union leaders have adopted just such an intelligent philosophy.

Union leadership knows well that change-overs are going to be hardest on the older workers, who will probably find it difficult to retrain themselves for the new work. They are putting this problem up to management and in most cases temporary jobs are being found to fill them in till retirement. In some cases, retirement at 60 instead of at 65 is the answer. Enlightened labor men know that management does not regard automation as unalloyed bliss, but rather as an expensive necessity carrying a high initial risk. They realize that business will be only too glad to share its automation problems and benefits with labor. The idea of "improper use, for narrow and selfish purposes" is just a trifle too reminiscent of bygone political days to make much sense. The people who talk about "economic royalists" and "malefactors of great wealth" haven't bought an automated factory lately, or had to foot the bills. Either they do not know what automation is all about, or they are talking for publication.

The error of some rather vociferous union people is that they expect to dictate the terms of a scientific advance. I respectfully doubt that the laws of nature and of human nature will permit.

We should not ignore the fact that manufacturing, the most fertile ground so far found for sprouting automation, provides only one job in four to American workers. Furthermore, the prediction is that the demand for goods and services in the next

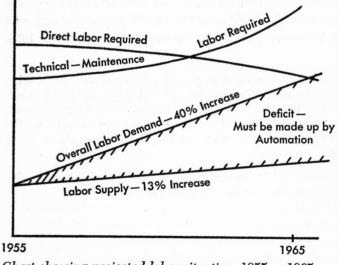

1955 1965

Chart showing projected labor situation, 1955 → 1965

ten years will soar by 40 per cent, while the total labor force available will increase by only 14 per cent. One reason given for this is that longevity is steadily increasing, which will put a larger proportion of our people beyond the working age. A second reason for the lag of labor forces is that more and more people are going to college, on their way to professional pursuits, which will prevent them from being artisans. Thus, the gravest problem ahead is to find men and women to work *outside* industry in the three-fourths of the labor force that will stand the heaviest brunt of progress: carpenters, plumbers, garage mechanics, barbers, bus drivers—an endless list of people who cannot be greatly helped by automation.

It is not selfishness or greed that is driving factory owners on toward automation, but the downright fear that they will not be able to meet the demand for their products if they don't use it fast enough.

Unless all economists and government statisticians are wrong, we shall, by 1975, be faced with a definite shortage of human labor on all fronts, that cannot be met without a wide exploitation of automatic machinery. Carroll W. Boyce, an editor of *Factory Management*, states it this way in the September, 1955, issue:

> If automation increases at its present rate, every available worker will have to be putting in 40 hours a week to keep raising our standard of living. But additional workers, to permit a shorter workweek, won't exist. So automation must come even faster to make up the deficit. Only alternative: Slow our progress toward higher living standards.

That we are all in for economic growing pains cannot be denied. The antidote, not the cause, is automation.

2

ERMA AND HER FRIENDS

15 | REVOLUTION ON PAPER

Automation's biggest job tomorrow probably will not be in manufacturing, but on the desks of the world, handling the trillions of pieces of paper which keep track of our lives. Year in and year out, virtually every activity of individuals and organizations has to be put on record in some kind of words and figures, then filed and forgotten, or kept in reserve. No purchase can be made today, no business transaction however slight, but must be washed by this paper flood. Sales slips, purchase orders, payrolls, insurance accounts, auto registrations, income and social-security tax returns, railroad and airplane and bus reservations, bank checks and statements—these are the sort of thing that make up the flood. According to a *Fortune* survey, some nine *billion* checks are cashed yearly in the United States; 26 million new farm mortgages and 78 million new insurance policies are written. Studies by the Hoover Commission reveal that two million government employes write more than 500 letters apiece every year—a cool billion. As many as a dozen copies of some of these are made and distributed.

Somebody has to inscribe every item of this gigantic tidal wave of wood pulp and ink marks. Not only that. Somebody has to transmit them, file them, compute the figures on them, add them, subtract them, blend them in with thousands of other

157

similar documents, check them, correct their errors, and use them to construct tomorrow's flood of paper. To do this today, it takes some eight million office people, working in one of the least rewarding jobs a human can do.

Their task is a discouraging one, too, for not very much has been done to give them mechanical aid. By and large, the job is a manual form of slavery, calling for a continuous small contribution of brain. It can only be done by sheer hours of work by people. There are, in fact, more clerical workers in this country than there are farmers, and almost as many of them as factory workers. "One dollar out of every eight, being spent on U.S. goods and services," says *Fortune,* "is now being paid to men and women who, in their daily work, produce nothing more intrinsically useful than marks on a piece of paper." *

It is true that there have long been a number of office machines that lighten the burden of the clerk: typewriters, adding machines, punch-card recording and data-processing systems, addressing machines, special files. But the main work of originating the paper flood and seeing that it all disperses to the right places is still a job for individuals "using their heads."

The end of this may be in sight. Automation, as it has done in the factory, *could* take over a large share of the burden. It could, moreover, modernize and streamline the routine itself, freeing countless people for pursuits that require more of judgment and imagination and less of habitual repetition.

Since there is so large a share of individual decision required for "manufacturing" the paper flood, automation, in the forms we have seen it so far, is not adequate. To relieve a burden on a human mind, a machine must itself possess a sort of mind. It must have a degree of judgment and discretion; it must store facts in vast quantities and be able to use them correctly; it

* Edmund L. Van Deusen, "The Coming Victory over Paper," *Fortune,* October, 1955.

must, like any human being, be able to track down its mistakes and eliminate them.

All this leads to automation's most complicated and versatile tool, the computer, or data-processing machine, sometimes called the "mechanical brain." We shall see a lot of the computer from now on, for it is invariably needed where the functions of the human brain are taken over or supplemented by machinery. But before we study it in detail, let us examine one at work.

In June, 1956, the first completely automated machine for handling routine paper work went into service in San Jose, California. All computers, for some obscure reason, have pronounceable names, and this one is ERMA. The national foible for turning initials into nicknames has got into the computer game the way Latin has invaded horticulture and medicine. ERMA stands for "Electronic Recording Machine—Accounting," and she is to be used in a branch of the Bank of America in San Jose. There she will require the day-long attention of five girls and one or two full-time technicians to keep her interior in good order. She will do the work that fifty girls with adding machines have been doing "by hand."

Let us see what the work is that ERMA has taken over. Her job is, pure and simple, the task of handling checks that come into the bank, withdrawing the funds of the depositors. She will handle deposits, too. ERMA was built by the laboratories of the Stanford Research Institute at Palo Alto and cost two million dollars. She required five years of study and experiment and final building.

When a check is drawn by a depositor in payment of a bill, the recipient sends it to his own bank. From here it goes on to a clearing house in the region and eventually returns to the depositor's bank for final accounting. Upon receipt, the amount on the check must be subtracted from his current balance and the new total of his account posted in the bank's records. At the

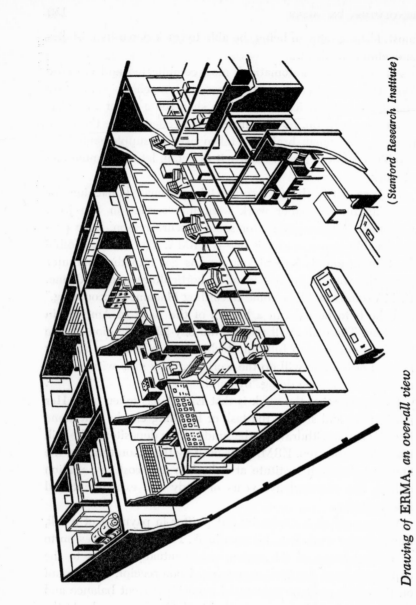

Drawing of ERMA, an over-all view

end of the month, the bank must gather together all of this depositor's checks and deposit slips, compile a statement of them, work out his month-end balance, and return the lot to him. For a large number of depositors, this routine is so severe that it keeps the bank personnel busy at accounting typewriters every minute of every working day. No small part of the job is the verifying of every item to eliminate all errors.

As the first of her line, ERMA has only a modest capacity. She can attend to 38,000 accounts and no more. The next model, already in the works, is planned for 50,000. Her employers say that unless such bookkeeping machines are put in, it will presently become impossible to expand their banks to keep up with the flood of new customers. There would not be enough women clerks available to do the increased work by hand.

If you go into ERMA's own special building in San Jose you will find a quiet front office, more like an electric-light company, say, than a bank. Behind a long glass panel you see a row of five curved desks, each one flanked by sloping control panels decked out with rows of buttons and lights. At each of these "consoles" sits a girl with a basket of checks beside her. She picks one up, reads it quickly, punches something on the keyboard and drops the check in a slot nearby. Then she picks up another. Her companions are doing the same.

Looking over the shoulder of one of these girls, the operation seems absurdly simple. Physically, it is. Mentally, the act of reading the check and putting it in the slot is something that science has not been able to teach ERMA to do. What her attendant does, merely, is to read the amount of money which the depositor wrote across the front of the check in his own handwriting. This amount she punches out on the keyboard. At the same time, for verifying purposes, she reads a special number that is printed across the bottom of the check. Then she drops the check into the slot. Almost instantaneously, a register in front of her repeats that code number before her.

ERMA has already gone to work on the check, by "reading" the number and displaying it. She is asking the girl if the reading is correct. If it is, we are all set. It is, for ERMA is not one to make little careless mistakes. So the girl presses the "entry bar" on her keyboard and ERMA goes into the complicated process of "digesting" the check, giving her attendant a little green light by way of a nod.

Checks issued to depositors at ERMA's branch of the Bank of America look like any other checks except for two things: that code number on the front and a group of short black lines

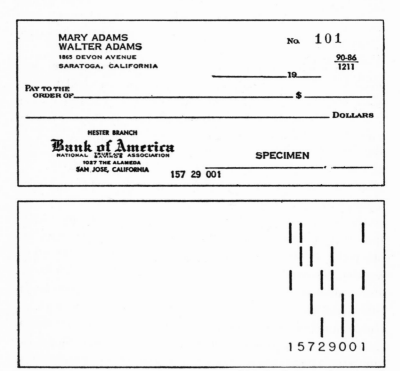

(*Stanford Research Institute*)

Sample check for ERMA

on the back. ERMA doesn't read ordinary Arabic numerals, but she readily understands this set of dashes on the back, which she reads the moment the check is in place in the console slot. The marks are printed in magnetic ink. ERMA brushes a magnet over them, activates them, "reads" them electronically, and tells what she saw on her register above, all in a small fraction of a second. This number she has read, plus the amount of the check, which her attendant had to read for her, are all the data she requires, except for the information as to whether the slip of paper is a withdrawal or a deposit. The girl touches one more button to signify that it is a check to be debited against the depositor's account, say for $45.00.

Let us say that the number read by ERMA was 15729001. That means, simply, that the check originated from Branch Bank No. 157, and that a certain depositor, Miss Mary Adams, holding the number 29001, is the one to be involved in this transaction.

Now let's see what ERMA can do with the information. In the flash of an instant after the check was read, ERMA's miles of wiring have transmitted the number in coded impulses to a whirling magnetic drum, which is called her "memory." On the drum, also in code, are the necessary facts about every account in the bank. But ERMA, for the moment, is interested in only one—that of Mary Adams, No. 29001. By electronic selection, she picks out the particular "address" on the drum reserved for current information about this depositor's balance, "looks up" the amount stored there, and transmits it—still in code—to another part of her anatomy known as the "arithmetic unit." In the meanwhile, other channels have transmitted the $45.00 amount of Mary Adams' check to this same unit. When the two figures meet—always in code—a subtraction is automatically performed and a remainder obtained. This remainder flashes back to the drum, wipes out the previous balance and takes

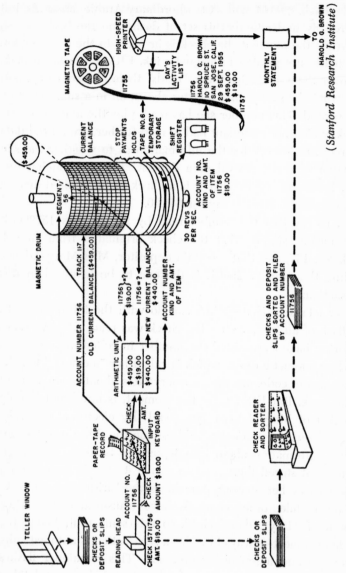

Diagram of ERMA showing a typical check transaction

(*Stanford Research Institute*)

its place. There it will stay undisturbed until Mary Adams sends through another check or deposit.

These are the bare bones of the operation, but there are many other features too. First of all, ERMA must know whether there is a stop-payment order out against this check or a hold-funds order against the account. People sometimes write a check, then think better of it and notify the bank to refuse payment on it. Or, a certified check may be outstanding against the account, requiring guaranteed funds to meet it. When such a thing occurs, an operator gives the necessary information to ERMA and she tucks it in a separate section of her magnetic memory, neatly tagged with Mary Adams' number. One of her first duties when the check information arrives in her memory is to search this special file to see if such an order has been recorded. If it has, she signals back to her operator something like, "Miss Adams doesn't want this check paid," or "If I pay $45.00 I won't have enough to meet the hold order on Adams." In either event, ERMA declines to tinker with Miss Adams' balance and account adjustments are made by hand.

The vast majority of transactions, of course, run into no such trouble, and the ordinary checks and deposit slips go through ERMA in just under one second. In the meantime, the four other operators are feeding her checks also. Because of the enormous extent and agility of her memory, the robot can be working on many separate checks at once without mixing them up. She can keep the five girls busy without once stubbing her toe. If interference does occur anywhere, she will signal a delay to one girl and complete the work for another. The longest delay possible is one second.

Nor is this all that ERMA has to do. In addition to her regular and special memories she has a temporary storage file. Here the Adams account number and this latest withdrawal of $45.00 have been entered at the same time her regular memory got them. Meanwhile, many other pieces of similar information are coming in from our operator and the four others. Temporary storage is capable of holding several hours' worth of transactions. As it fills up, ERMA's electronic brain notices the fact and prepares to send these figures to her permanent storage department.

This last is a group of reels of magnetic tape, long enough to contain sections devoted to all depositors. At any moment Mary Adams' section of the tape will contain, in coded form, her number, name, address, and the full details of all money transactions she has had so far that month.

When ERMA's channels are clear to do so, she picks up from the temporary storage file whatever new depositor figures have accumulated in it. These she transfers to the proper place on the tape, according to name, and in proper order. This operation involves a bit of hard work for ERMA—a complicated electronic manipulation—but does not preoccupy her at all. While her circuits are filling tape, she is still going on at full speed with her five operators.

When the Adams check has finally been recorded on tape, ERMA takes a look at the transaction to be sure she has made no mistakes. This she does by independent adding and subtracting. With the sum proved, she prints back before the operator a slip showing the whole arithmetical procedure. This is a necessary final verification, and goes with the Adams check into the bank's records.

ERMA's remaining duties are in connection with preparing the depositors' statements. At the end of each day she runs through all the balances and makes sure that everything is up to date on the tape and in her main memory. Then, on the last day of the banking month she subtracts from each account whatever service charge there may have been. This in itself is no light matter, being reckoned from a formula which includes the size of the balance, the activity of the account, and the type of account it is. ERMA's arithmetic unit does the work.

During the subsequent few days, ERMA requires a trifle of outside help. Live clerks remove the reels of magnetic tape from her permanent file and place them in a high-speed printer. At the staggering rate of one complete statement every two-and-a-half seconds, this automatic typewriter clears away the entire job for 38,000 depositors in about two days' working time. With former live-girl methods it took fifty humans, working from morning till night, *the whole month* to do this. This is why, in a big bank, you always see so much typing going on. And this is the reason for ERMA.

There is one clean-up operation that ERMA cannot do for herself: the sorting out of the individual checks which the five girls have processed during any one day. They fall entirely at random and of course have to be separated and arranged according to depositors, for final inclusion in the statement envelopes. This operation, too, is done in most banks by feminine fingers. When you consider that the estimated nine billion checks in America's banking year have to be looked at and processed an average of six times apiece on their travels through the system, you can see why banks are so anxious to mechanize.

At the request of the Bank of America, Stanford Research Institute tackled the problem of mechanizing this check-sorting job. The machine that resulted is to be found working alongside ERMA and easily keeping up with her. The sorter is a long framework, mounting a number of flat belts that speed along, carrying a river of checks with them. The papers travel at about 12 feet per second—as fast as you can run—and are snatched off the belts by arms that know unerringly where to put them, in various sorting bins. Let the Stanford people tell the story:

The check sorter has the same ability to read account numbers printed in magnetic ink on the checks as has the input section of the electronic bookkeeping machine (ERMA). The machine has 12 boxes or output compartments (0 through 9 plus two for rejected checks) into which it sorts the checks or deposit slips.

To sort checks, a bundle is first placed in the sorter. The top check is whisked off by a vacuum feeding device and guided to a scanning head that is manually set to read the first (units) digit of the account number. This information, i.e., whether the unit digit is a 0, 1, 2 or other number, is stored for a fraction of a second in a rotating mechanical memory device. Meanwhile, the check itself is being carried at the rate of 150 inches per second on a belt into the sorting section.

Mary Adams' account number is 29001. Hence, when the sorter comes to that check, the value of the digit is read as 1 and remembered by the memory mechanism. When the check approaches the number 1 compartment, the memory device causes a gate to open, sidetracking the check into that compartment.

In this manner all checks are sorted according to the units digit. Then the checks from each of the ten compartments are manually collected and run through the machine again, this time sorting for the tens digit. On this next pass Miss Adams' check goes into the 0 compartment. By sorting each bundle five times (once for each digit) the checks are placed in sequence by account number, and the items for any one account are in the order of processing by the bookkeeping machine.

The outstanding features of this device are not those of its basic principle of operation, which is relatively simple. The requirements of speed and accuracy are so high, however, as to generate engineering problems of a different order of magnitude. Account numbers are read and checks sorted at the rate of ten per second. A stack of a thousand checks about five inches high "melts" down in the input container in about one and one-half minutes. To obtain good accuracy at these speeds the paper is controlled pneumatically for both feeding and stacking, not by mechanical friction devices. The machine errors—checks sorted into wrong compartments—run less than one in 100,000. Rejects, or checks the machine cannot sort, are below one percent.

It is not too difficult to see what incredible problems have to be solved in order to invent machines to do the slave-labor for people. Professor Wiener's remark that people competing with slave-machines must work under slave conditions, seems to ignore the obvious fact that the highest order of brains and ingenuity are required to invent and service such machines.

16 | WHAT MAKES ERMA GO?

There are hundreds of computers more or less like ERMA, and thousands of jobs for them to do. As far as "brains" go, ERMA is not very high in the scale. She is strictly a special-purpose data-processing machine, fondly called "an idiot" in engineering circles. A rather special idiot, too, for she can understand nothing but slips of paper with magnetic lines on the back in a certain position. To train your dog to go out and pick up the morning paper represents a more sophisticated use of brain power than ERMA is capable of. Nevertheless, this robot is the first to be put into service to do a complete clerical task. As such, it is a good example to scrutinize closely. ERMA contains all of the basic elements of mechanical computing machines, though she is not very bright.

Reduced to flow diagrams, computers are simple enough. They possess at most five organs: an input mechanism, a storage or memory section, a computing or arithmetic device, a control or co-ordinating part, and an output section. This is as far as the simplicity goes.

Up to this point the machines resemble the automated manufacturing lines we have already met. The raw materials for a product go in at one end, are subjected to numerous forming processes in which memory and computing play a part, and

169

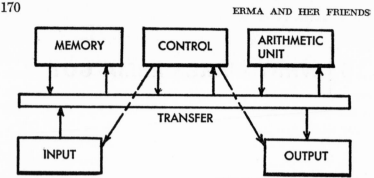

(*M.I.T. Computer Laboratory*)

Typical block diagram of computer

come out finished and checked at the other. In the case of the computer, the product, as well as the raw material, is *information.* ERMA's demand in these terms is merely two sets of figures—account number and amount of check, plus the character of the transaction, deposit or withdrawal, which can also be coded as a number. On its travels through the machine, this numerical information is worked upon and finally delivered as processed information, still in the form of numbers.

To accomplish this, ERMA, or any computer, must be made ready for duty by an act called "programming." The machine must be instructed in what it is to do. ERMA is a good one to start with in this regard because the directions given her are relatively simple and they do not change. Later, we shall see computers that understand "if," that is, that can make a choice between alternatives, depending on how the information received shapes up during processing. ERMA is free of that, except that if she finds a depositor's balance insufficient to meet the check, she says so, and quits. She has just enough judgment for that.

Programming for ERMA consists in building her various parts into electronic and mechanical channels which lead inevitably through a definite sequence from start to finish. By placing wires and electron tubes and relays in certain relations to each other, the engineers have, in effect, posted a standard set of commands to the machine. "When you receive three basic elements of information," they say, "do this to them. With the result you get, do that. When you are through, put the result away where you can find it when we want it."

How is this worked out in terms of "hardware"?

The input section of ERMA is the large keyboard at the console, combined with the slot in the desk top. (The five consoles work in parallel, like five marksmen shooting at the same target.) By depressing certain keys, the operator closes the switches to a number of electric circuits. This is the coding of the dollar amount on the check. At the same time, in the slot, the machine has "looked at" the magnetic bars on the back of the check, the positions of which mean definite numbers to it. Circuits have been activated by this, which operate locally to throw up numbers on the register in front of the operator. The input operation is now complete.

The actual situation is that a long row of switches inside the console are readied, either to permit current to flow or to prevent it. If a particular switch is closed, it means that the number associated with it is called for. If it is open, that number is not called for. ERMA has a row of figures nineteen digits long. She can accept account numbers of eight figures and dollar amounts up to $999,999,999.99—eleven figures more. In addition to the figures, there are several columns of buttons—to check errors, ask for a bank balance, add in service charges, and so on.

Now the operator pushes down her entry bar, which is a final switch allowing all the others to function. ERMA generates *pulses* of current something like heartbeats, but infinitely faster. It is one of these pulses that finds its way through the pattern of switches and passes inside to the memory drum and to the arithmetic unit. Let us look at the memory first.

All computers have memories of some kind. Their purpose is to store numerical information so that it can be found and used. Mechanical memory devices touch our lives constantly. An electric wall switch is a memory device. The actual remembering unit is a spring and a lever. If you snap the switch bar in the "on" direction, the spring "remembers" to hold it there until you snap it to the "off" position. This switch has a "two-track mind," in that it can remember two different things you may want it to do: light on, light off.

ERMA's memory is a magnetic drum, a very popular type at present. It is a two-track mind, for it can remember when you said yes, and when you said no, like the light switch. The magnetic memory drum consists of a cylinder of non-magnetic material, coated with a plastic containing very finely divided iron oxide, which is magnetic. The drum spins at high speed all the time, close beneath rows of small electromagnets. If any of these is energized for a moment, it leaves a tiny spot of magnetized material on the drum. This spot will stay put indef-

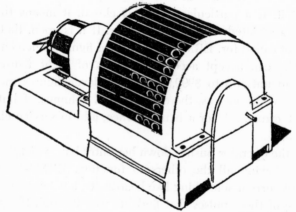

(*Remington-Rand*)

Typical magnetic memory

initely, or until it is rubbed out by a *de*-magnetizing impulse from the electromagnet.

ERMA's drum makes 30 revolutions a second. As its circumference is about 50 inches and its length 20, it has surface enough to accommodate an enormous number of separate magnetic spots—a million and a half of them by actual count. Each of these spots, either magnetized or not magnetized, is said to contain one "bit" of information. The arrangement of the electromagnets is such that bits are stored in ring-shaped zones around the drum, 300 rings side by side, with space for 5000 bits in each ring. The locations of the bits can thus be divided up into what the technicians call "addresses." Give the machine an address consisting of a certain ring and a certain point on that ring, and it can find any one of the million-and-a-half bits *in 1/30th of a second.* The information which has to do with Mary Adams, or any other depositor, is located at a certain address on the drum and consists of a string of bits of *magnetic* information. By activating the right electromagnets from the input data, ERMA can either "read" what is contained at a specific address, or she can introduce new material, after rubbing out the old.

When the operator starts ERMA going, the numbers are coded into the "binary" system of counting (which we shall examine in a moment) and fed through the switches to the appropriate electromagnets around the memory drum. The first part of the job is to find out what the amount of Miss Adams' balance is; so the electromagnets are activated to read what is on the drum at her address. It is something like your going to the post office and looking at the front of your box, say 4085, to see if there is any mail in it. Either there is or there isn't, and you act accordingly.

Now we come to the secret of the computer's great speed. The switch on your wall and the electronic circuits inside ERMA can do either of two things: they can make a contact, or not make one. The same is true of the magnetic spots on the drum. At any given location, there *is* a spot or there *isn't*. This is the same thing as if you printed the word "yes" or the word "no" at that location. Thus, the work of this type of computer— called a "digital" machine—is merely that of playing intricate games with a vast number of yeses and noes. Such a game is right down the line for electronics. A vacuum-tube pair, called a "flip-flop," can be made to close a circuit or open it. All it needs is a tiny pulse of current to do it.

So, as the depositor's account information, in the form of a string of numbers, comes through from the operator's console, it is converted into a series of yes-and-no conditions in a large number of electronic circuits. Actually, since ERMA plays a yes-no game exclusively, her internal workings do not use the numerals from 0 to 9, but only the figures 0 and 1. This is called the "binary" system, and it is used by computers and in automation everywhere. At the console, ERMA understands how to change decimal system numbers into binary. Once she has done that, she has no further use for our common form of notation until her high-speed printer brings them to light again in the final bank statements.

The binary system, or code, is simply a trick with numbers— a method of arranging 0's and 1's in such a way that they stand for any of the common numerals that we use every day. Once they are so arranged, any sum in arithmetic that can be done in decimal notation can also be done in binary notation. In terms of electronics, this means that yes-no circuits can add, subtract, multiply, and divide as handily as you and I can with all ten digits.

You can arrange a table of conversion from decimal to binary numbers very simply, by following one rule—that when you have tallied up the first 0 and 1, you must begin again, by shifting the next 1 into the next column to the left. In the decimal system you shift to the left when you have used up the figure 9.

Mathematically, this is a scheme for employing the powers of 2 instead of the powers of 10. In the 10 system, you count from 0 to 9, then begin at 0 again, "carrying" a 1 into the next place to the left. This gives you 10, or the first power of 10. Continuing to count, you arrive at 99. Add one more and you come up with 1 again, in the *third* place to the left, with two zeros—the second power of 10. And so on, moving one place to the left for every added power of 10.

In the binary system you begin counting with a 0 at the extreme right, then replace it with a 1. Then, instead of putting down a 2 in place of the 1, you write in a 0 and carry a 1 to the next left place, producing 10 (read it "one-O"). This signifies the first power of 2. To count 3 you retain the 1 in the second place to the left, and replace the 0 in the first place with a 1, to read 11 (call it "one-one"). To count 4, you again shift to the left, writing 100 (signifying the *second* power of 2). It takes quite a lot more places to count to high numbers in binary then it does in decimal—something like three times as many. But if each place is represented by a vacuum-tube pair it is simple enough. Tubes are cheap and reliable and work faster than thought.

Say you have five tube-pairs, representing the ability to count to five places, reading from right to left. In the binary system 0 would thus appear as 00000, that is, all tubes off, or saying no-no-no-no-no. 1 would appear as 00001; 2 as 00010; 3 as 00011; 4 as 00100; 5 as 00101; and so on. Five places will count up to 31, which would be written on paper as 11111, or yes-yes-yes-yes-yes. Six tube-pairs will count to 63; seven to 127; eight to 255; nine to 511; and ten to 1023. Each number will count to one *less* than that particular power of 2. Twenty places will count to more than a million. The accompanying table

A TABLE OF DECIMAL-BINARY EQUIVALENTS

Ordinary Numbers	Equivalent Powers of 2	Number of Tube Pairs	Binary Notation	Can Count Up To—
1	2^0	1	1	1
2	2^1	2	10	3
4	2^2	3	100	7
8	2^3	4	1,000	15
16	2^4	5	10,000	31
32	2^5	6	100,000	63
64	2^6	7	1,000,000	127
128.	2^7	8	10,000,000	255
256	2^8	9	100,000,000	511
512	2^9	10	1,000,000,000	1,023
1,024	2^{10}	11	10,000,000,000	2,047
2,048	2^{11}	12	100,000,000,000	4,095
4,096	2^{12}	13	1,000,000,000,000	8,191
8,192	2^{13}	14	10,000,000,000,000	16,383
16,384	2^{14}	15	100,000,000,000,000	32,767
32,768	2^{15}	16	1,000,000,000,000,000	65,535
65,536	2^{16}	17	10,000,000,000,000,000	131,071
131,072	2^{17}	18	100,000,000,000,000,000	262,143
262,144	2^{18}	19	1,000,000,000,000,000,000	524,287
524,288	2^{19}	20	10,000,000,000,000,000,000	1,048,575
1,048,576	2^{20}	21	100,000,000,000,000,000,000	2,097,151

shows this graphically. You can get a fascinating stimulation out of a paper and pencil and the binary notation. Adept at it in its simplest form, you can go on to more intricate arrangements, using powers of 3, 4, 5, and up to 10 and beyond. Or, you can base the whole thing on a constant, such as 1, calling zero 00001, and going on up from there. ERMA does this, in fact. Her designers adopted the idea because then ERMA will not confuse what is meant as a zero with the fact that her girls have all gone home. That is, she can distinguish between the digit zero and being shut down for the night.

Everything ERMA does from here on conforms to the yes-no pattern. You might say that she plays a game of Twenty Questions with herself, asking for information and getting only yes-or-no answers. When her magnetic drum is first consulted for Mary Adams' account balance, address circuits are automatically chosen that will look in the right area of the drum. The electromagnets associated with her "street and number" are alerted by being connected to the arithmetic unit. As the drum sweeps around, the host of small magnetic spots associated with the Adams account convey to the electromagnets a pattern of pulses, by electromagnetic induction. These pulses, now in the form of small electrical voltages, are what actually go to the arithmetic unit. Perhaps it will take hundreds of these bits of information to convey the message, but it will all be there, crowded into a small fraction of a second.

We now come to the work of the arithmetic unit, which is not a drum but an array of panels mounting thousands of vacuum-tube yes-no switches and many miles of wiring. This unit has just received a binary-coded message from the console expressing the amount of the Adams check—$45.00. It now receives a binary message from the memory section, saying, perhaps, that the Adams balance is $500.00. The subtracting operation is not difficult. For example, if you had the sum *three minus two* to do, you could write it as 00011 minus 00010. Performing this you would get 00001, which stands for 1 in the ordinary decimal system. More complicated subtractions are done in similar fashion, using a "carry" technique identical with the one we learned in grade school.

In any case, the subtraction of figures, even if they run to the 11 places for which there is room on the console board, takes only a few thousandths of a second, electronically. If the result should be a negative amount—an overdrawn account—a special circuit is brought into play and the news is flashed back to the operator in the form of a red light. Otherwise, the new balance goes back to the memory.

It is to be understood that the electromagnets on the memory have two functions. In the first they "listen" for the pattern of magnetic spots already there, taking *out* information. In the second, they first wipe the section clean with a short jolt of alternating current, as is done in your home tape recorder. Then they flash a series of pulses onto the drum, putting a new pattern of magnetic spots in place. This is information going *in*. One pulse of current, lasting a few millionths of a second, is enough to establish a magnetic spot.

The error test, which ERMA always makes when she computes anything, is done by separate circuits, which repeat the calculations, first by adding, then by subtracting back again and matching the results obtained with those it is desired to verify. If there is an error, the arithmetic unit goes over the sum again. If the error persists, it signals the maintenance board that something is wrong. By the nature of the signal the attendant can tell where the trouble lies.

The remainder of ERMA's job on the Adams check is to transfer the transaction to her temporary storage memory, also on one of the two magnetic drums which she has, alter the Adams balance according to instructions from the arithmetic unit, and signal the result back to the operator, causing it to be printed on a length of paper tape. Since the entire sequence of actions has been done by electrons, which travel at nearly the speed of light, it hasn't taken very long. By far the greatest time-waster ERMA has to put up with is her whirling magnetic memory. It takes 1/30th of a second for her to look up or to file information on it, which is so "slow" that many more talented machines use all-electronic memories. However, ERMA isn't so bad. Her elapsed time of less than one second for a transaction is fast enough to care for the business of a large bank without hurrying.

As digital computers go, ERMA is fairly compact. She occupies a total of about 4000 square feet—a space 40 feet wide and 100 feet long. Her total weight is about 25 tons. Her two 40-foot cabinets of equipment include over 42,000 electron tubes and take some 60 kilowatts of electric power. An air-conditioning plant is necessary to keep her temperature down to normal. Although the backs of the panels are a fantastic tangle of small wires—there are a million feet of them—in front they look smooth and neat. Groups of vacuum tubes and their circuits are contained in small metal boxes which can be pulled out for replacement in a few seconds. ERMA's crew of technicians makes regular tests on her from top to toe, usually at night. Most failures occur in the tubes, which gradually weaken and burn out. To guard against such failure during working hours, the tube banks are tested at a lower-than-normal voltage, which quickly reveals the weak tubes. By this servicing system, daytime failures are very rare indeed.

One final thing about ERMA we must not skip: she is learning to read figures just as ordinary people do, rather than pick them up from magnetic marks on the back of a check. This is called "character recognition," and is one of the latest advances in mechanical brains. We shall hear of it again with more advanced computers. ERMA, as she now stands, can't do this trick; the Stanford Research engineers, however, have built an experimental number-reader for sorting traveler's checks, whose principles will be incorporated in ERMA's descendants.

Character recognition is a matter of "scanning." It is based on the fact that if a numeral is printed in magnetic ink and then rushed through a magnetic reader, an electrical wave-form results that is peculiar to that one numeral. Electronic devices recognize the particular wave as it is generated and convert it to binary bits of information signifying the numeral.

As you will remember from using traveler's checks, each one has a long number printed in the upper right-hand corner. This is the number the issuing bank wants to know quickly and record as soon as the check comes back from circulation. The sorting job has always been done by girls looking at the checks and typing up a list of the numbers as they read them. The new machine does the same thing, only faster: one girl operating it can record a hundred checks a minute.

The great virtue of the new robot, besides its speed, is that it can read numbers that have become completely illegible to humans. Ink blots, dirt, fingermarks, tears mended with Scotch tape, crumpling—none of them faze the check-reader at all.

The machine is something like 50 times as accurate as the human eye. But to make it still more foolproof, an ingenious trick is added that only a computer could do. Ordinarily, there are 10 numbers on a traveler's check. The checks for use with this machine will have an 11th number at the right-hand end of the string, so chosen that the sum of all 11 numbers can be divided by 9. As the machine reads, its arithmetic unit adds up the numerals and divides by 9 (the same thing in a computer's brain as *subtracting* 9 as many times as possible). If anything is left over, it knows it has made a mistake and throws out the check, for special study by the operator.

We should note here that the fifty girls who have been displaced by ERMA have all got better jobs with the same bank. Many of them were advanced to tellers. There are never enough women available for such positions, but when ERMA's family really takes over, there will be.

17 | ALPHABET GONE MAD

UNIVAC, ENIAC, MANIAC, SAGE; SEAC, ERMA, and RAM. These alphabetic monsters run all the way from Babbage's Difference Engine and Kelvin's Tide Predictor to SAGE, the latest, which undertakes to predict and head off the Russians. If man has anywhere succeeded in shifting his burdens to machines, surely his greatest success is with computers. They are no longer news. Practically anybody can tell you that a "mechanical brain" can solve a problem in a few minutes that would take a human being his lifetime. Stuart Chase has said whimsically that IBM's 701 computer is 100,000 times as fast at arithmetic as he is himself. "After receiving 963 instructions, the 701 can calculate the path of a guided missile, performing 1,100,000 calculations in two minutes. This calculation I could toss off in a matter of 15 years." *

But what can computers actually do? It seems to be the unvarying habit of popular apologists for these machines to explain that they can multiply and divide numbers at the rate of 2000 times a second, and add and subtract at 16,000 times a second. Is this all they can do? And who needs any such numerical wizardry when the real problems of engineering

* Stuart Chase, "Machines That Think," *Reader's Digest*, January, 1954.

181

are intricate mathematical equations? The answer is that while computers can do little more than execute these simple kinds of arithmetic at colossal speed, most tough mathematical problems can be broken down into just such simple sums. Their speed and accuracy are their real reason for being.

North American Aviation, Inc., one of the largest builders of military planes, says that in theory, a few modern computers can take the place of 500,000 engineers. What they mean, of course, is that the machines can do routine work equal to that accomplished by so many men working with pencil and paper. The guided-missile problem Stuart Chase mentions is really a vast routine undertaking—setting up a formula and then computing results for a huge number of different conditions. North American points out that several of its latest fighter planes have been "designed in computing machines." The procedure is to work out equations which tell what a given component, such as a wing, will do under all sorts of speeds, altitudes, turns, etc., and then "fly it in the computer." That is, let the computer figure answers to the equation for all possible values of the variables. Tens of thousands of designs can thus be examined quickly, and the few that are good will show up at once. A few years ago even this large organization could do the figuring on no more than 100 designs "by hand." There simply wasn't time. Now, in a problem like this the best design can be reached with little human contribution beyond judging the validity of the results.

A very large majority of intricate mathematical problems can be handled in this way, by putting a computer through thousands or millions of steps in sequence. All you want to know, for instance, is whether it will rain or not next Sunday at the beach, or whether you should go on your vacation in July or August, to catch the best weather. Scientists have predicted the weather for a century or more, but haven't come out very well, certainly not with long-range prediction. The reason is that the air above us is an ocean with a vast number of currents, high pressures and low, temperature gradients, fronts, winds, barometric differences, cloud formations, not to mention a staggering variety of local anomalies that don't seem to follow any rules at all. Real prediction would mean a complete mapping of *all* these factors, and the solution of an equation containing them, for each city in the United States. It could never be done by pencil and paper, but there is some hope that with a big enough computer, and enough data-gathering stations, it can eventually be done mechanically. Such work is of vital interest to the military, to agriculture, and to science itself. The U.S. Weather Bureau has made a start and mathematicians are working on formulas that will give reliable results. The month-long forecasts you see in the newspapers are the first attempts at employing these man-and-computer teams. Data-gathering by radar seems to be the most promising avenue of research.

The designers of cameras have a similar chore of routine calculation in order to arrive at a good lens. You don't simply look a lens form up in a book. You *figure* it. I once saw the dossier of calculations for a lens for a five-dollar camera. It was a book of some 500 pages, completely covered with figures. It had occupied the optical engineer who did it several months. He had had to take into account many variables, such as focal length, definition, errors of many sorts, influence of different types of glass, depth of focus, cost, and so on. He had started with a chosen value of one variable and then tried out his equations by substituting various values for all the other variables. Eventually, he had tracked down the best combination of factors, and the lens was made accordingly.

Now, with a computer, you can "take a million different lenses out and shoot pictures with them" merely by telling the machine to use a certain formula and try out everything imaginable. The "brain" will do it so fast that the best possible compromise will show up in a few hours or days. Most of the time is spent in programming the machine with sufficiently good instructions.

During the war I visited ENIAC, the first really fast electronic computer, invented and built by the University of Pennsylvania. ENIAC was being financed by the Army's Bureau of Ordnance. When a gunner "lays" his gun on a distant target, all he does is to set his sighting-telescope cross hairs on the target. But the telescope is not connected directly to the gun. In between are scales and adjustments that must be made to include many variables such as the type of shell and propellant used, facts about the weather, and the motions of target and firing vehicle. Some of this data is the result of extremely complicated figuring which the firing officer couldn't possibly do on the job. So he refers to a set of firing tables worked out in advance to give the answers immediately. These firing tables, in those days, were occupying battalions of girls many months, figuring a schedule for each new type of weapon and ammunition. Changes in ordnance were coming so fast that the firing tables could not be prepared in time.

ENIAC, which could figure firing tables complete in a few minutes, got the Ordnance people out of a jam. Once programmed with the basic formulas, one or two operators could feed in the facts of each new missile, by means of punched cards, and pull out punched cards with the answers immediately.

The apparently simple problem of setting up a long-distance telephone call has become so difficult that the telephone company has embarked upon a scheme of using computers to do it. This is true automation, for the machine not only finds the best route and the circuits that are not in use, but does all the connecting and ringing, too. Everywhere, life is becoming so complicated that we could not live today without computers to solve these incredibly complex problems. Nor could wars be fought without them. I once asked General Leslie R. Groves, famous "bulldozer" of the atomic-bomb program, how he would solve the scientific problems in a new war. "First," he said, "I would order six UNIVAC's. Then I would requisition the services of all the large computers in the country."

Computers can, by solving problems in *logic,* make vital decisions, once they have been given the facts. The staggering decisions that General Groves made, as head of the Manhattan Engineer District, were largely done on hunch that this or that was right, and that anyway, there was no time for exhaustive study of the probabilities of success or failure. Several methods of making atomic explosives had to be authorized at the same time, in order to hit one that would surely work. That inspired guesswork produced the bomb, at fantastic expense. Such trial-and-error methods would never be used again. Supplied with the known facts of a military problem, a team of computers could work out the best possible methods of achieving any military result. It has even been suggested that world wars could be fought entirely by computers. A machine could tell whether a battle would be won or lost, given the relative military strengths, and other data concerning the contestants. They could be won, for that matter, by two opposing generals playing checkers with international victory as the stake. Neither method, unfortunately, it likely to be tried. Nevertheless, the side with the best computers and the sharpest knowledge of how to use them, is the one that is pretty sure to win next time.

Computers, then, can make decisions as well as add and subtract. It is for this reason that the two largest makers of such mechanical giants. International Business Machines Corporation and the Remington-Rand Division of Sperry-Rand Corporation, are vigorously promoting their use by business executives. Under modern business conditions these leaders must have *consolidated information* before them at all times.

Often, the information comes in at the last minute and decisions must be built on hunch and experience rather than on carefully winnowed essential facts. The case of a company preparing to open a new chemical plant is typical. Say that there are a dozen cities where it could be built, but in all of them conditions like labor supply, water, weather, city ordinances, transportation, closeness to markets, living accommodations, and the like are all different. At present the choice would be made, in all probability, after a round-table discussion, where personal preferences would carry too much weight. If the groundwork were to be laid down first by a computer, showing how each factor would influence the final result—if, picturesquely stated, the plant were to be "built" in each of the candidate cities and "operated" there—then the decision based on these comparative data could be relied upon to give the best possible location for that chemical plant.

The danger in intuitive decisions is that they must be based, largely, on subconscious awareness of past history. The future is likely to be different from the past, yet it is always for the future that decisions are made. A computer can work fast enough to utilize great quantities of up-to-the-minute data that no company has time to analyze by hand.

There are estimated to be upwards of 100 large computers in service or on order in the United States. Abroad there are between 30 and 50 more. Companies building them are sprouting everywhere. We are in process of generating another typical American boom, with the slogan "Let ERMA Do It" as the goal. In a few years no company of large or medium size will dare be without a computer or at least without access to one.

Genealogically, there are two branches to the computer family, technically known as "analogue" and "digital" machines. Their common heritage is mathematics: both accept problems expressed in terms of figures, and come out with answers also expressed in figures. Both operate with remarkable similarity to the human mind in that they "remember" facts given to them and use them to draw conclusions according to orderly processes of logic. Hence they are loosely called "brains." The interesting question of whether they *think* or not, we will tackle later. At the moment, for us, they are machines that can perform calculations at staggering speed. Even the slide rule, which is a simple analogue computer, is hundreds of times faster than paper-and-pencil calculation.

An analogue computer does its work by actually constructing a model of the problem you want solved. This model, called an *analogue*, is usually an arrangement of mechanical or electrical parts representing physical quantities, all of which can vary. These parts are tied together so as to interact in the same way that the elements of the problem do. Thus, if you wanted to know how long it would take a boat to fill up and sink if it had a certain-sized hole in it, you could construct an analogue of the situation (once you had worked out a proper formula describing it). A series of turning shafts with gears, a mechanical arrangement of springs and levers, or a group of electric circuits could do the job. By turning a crank, or by throwing

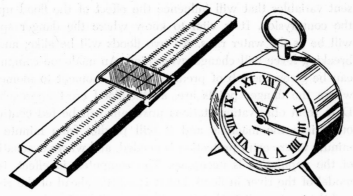

A slide rule is a simple analogue device   A clock counts, therefore it is a
                                               type of digital computer

a series of switches, you could cause the elements of the analogue to vary, and if a meter needle was placed at the output end to indicate results, you could learn how much water would be in the boat at any instant and how many minutes or hours it would take for her to sink.

What you get is a progressive solution of a complicated equation with many variables in it, and the problem you are solving is one that can be done on paper by using the calculus—a long job sometimes, but one which the analogue computer can whisk through in seconds. Most types of mathematical equation can be represented by a suitable analogue, hence these machines are built to serve one type or group of types.

The analogue computer has the advantage that it will yield a continuous solution of a problem if you manipulate the variable components while it is working on the solution. Such machines make wide use of selsyns and electronic switches, as well as of mechanical devices such as gears, contacting disks, cams, levers, etc.

Suppose you have a river like the Mississippi, which threatens a serious flood. It has many variables, such as levees of different heights, sand bars, bends, dams and all of them present variables that will influence the effect of the flood upon the countryside. It is vital to know where the danger spots will be as the water rises. No two floods will be alike, and a breaking levee will change everything. An analogue computer can be given the job of predicting, from moment to moment, where the danger points are, as the flood crest approaches. Data from observation stations upstream will be fed continuously into the machine and it will predict from minute to minute where extra protection is needed, and where evacuation of the population is necessary. The computer, in effect, is a model of the river in flood, but it is a little ahead of the river and thus can predict what the situation will be, in advance.

The great telescope dome at Palomar, in California, uses an

analogue device to control the motion of the dome so as to expose the 200-inch telescope to the star under observation. In a glass case, the computer, simulating the elements of the big machine around it, transmits to the dome motors the necessary orders to move and stop as may be needed.

Analogue computers are used in scores of military applications, such as automatic-firing devices on planes and on anti-aircraft guns. A little-known but important one is the computer serving Project Typhoon, which was built by the Radio Corporation of America to work out the performance of guided missiles, submarines, aircraft, and in fact, any moving object subject to many variable conditions. Much smaller analogue computers are used as gun directors. Here, they are able to combine all the variables such as target speed and course, wind, etc., and continuously aim the gun so that it will place its shells at the right spot in the sky to do the most damage.

This is a case of a computer tied in with automation. If the machine is fed by radar observations, it becomes wholly automatic. A still more advanced step, not much talked about, is the radar-computer combination which acts upon the probability of what the enemy pilot will do next in the way of evasive tactics. Going still one step farther, we have the proximity fuse, celebrated in the war. This one was a computer no bigger than a teacup, installed in the nose of the shell itself. Presumably the principle has been developed to a degree that makes a miss well-nigh impossible.

The modern analogue computer was historically the first mechanical brain to appear, and dates back to the 1930's, when Dr. Vannevar Bush at M.I.T. built the first successful "differential analyzer." Bush's laboratory had been studying the problem for more than 15 years. The present author was lucky enough to invent and build one of the elementary prototypes himself, under Dr. Bush's guidance.

Special analogue devices, indeed, go back a long way—at

least to Lord Kelvin's "tide engine," invented toward the end of the nineteenth century. This was a large wooden frame supporting a complicated set of gears, pulleys, and weights, with means for entering data concerning the influence of the sun, moon, and earth on the rise and fall of the tides. It was used to predict high and low water in London and other seaports. The Kelvin engine was a true analogue computer. Though somewhat crude, it has been in use with little change all over the world ever since, until recent improvements put it in the science museum.

The tide predictor showed up the inherent limitations of the analogue machine. It is a *measuring* device and there are always errors in measurement. When a number of physical quantities depend upon one another, their individual errors may add up to a larger error in the results. It was this limitation and the need for calculating complicated numerical problems at high speed, that produced the *digital* type of computer. This, too, goes back a long way—all the way, in fact, to the ten fingers on the hands of the cave men. When they learned to count up to ten, they established the base-10 system which we still use. The word *digit*, of course, derives from the Latin word for finger. The computer has borrowed the term. Some 5000 years ago, tallying by means of pebbles or small sticks gave rise to the famous abacus, or rack of beads, invented in the Orient. The abacus is still used in China—and in thousands of Chinese laundries in America, too. Even today it can outstrip the desk calculator in the hands of a native expert.

The first machine for calculating was probably Pascal's adding device, bearing the date 1642. Thirty years later Leibnitz enlarged its scope by making it multiply as well as add. These machines were more or less stunts turned out by two of history's great mathematicians. Even in 1833, when Charles Babbage invented his "difference engine," the machine was not practical. He did not build one, because he could not get accurate enough workmanship done. However, in 1887, Felt patented the "comptometer" and thus opened the age of mechanical calculation. Descendants of the comptometer are very much alive today in the host of desk adding machines we use so often. They are all digital computers of an elementary sort.

The digital computer is, pure and simple, a *counter*. It can do nothing but add and subtract, in definite steps of one digit each. It does not measure anything and hence does not produce approximately correct results. It is either right or wrong. At first glance, an overgrown adding machine would not seem to be very valuable as a mathematical tool. But consider what you can do with addition. The product of 2 times 2 is merely the addition of 2 to 2, *once*. If you want to multiply 2 by 4, you can simply take four 2's and add them. To multiply 576 by 88, you add 576 to itself 87 times. By longhand it would be absurdly slow to do that. But if an electronic machine gets the job, running through each addition in a few millionths of a second, the whole process is crammed into a jiffy.

By the same token, subtracting can be made to do sums in division. In similar fashion you can get squares and square roots, or any higher power you wish, merely by having the machine keep at it. There are very few mathematical problems, even the most advanced, which cannot be broken down into parts that can be solved by the four basic arithmetic operations we learned in school. The one basic requirement in using a digital computer is to know how to program your problem so that the computer can do it by arithmetic. Often this is not easy; it may take weeks or months, but it usually can be done.

The young engineer who took me through Whirlwind, the famous digital machine at M.I.T., joked about this. "I felt like kicking that darn thing the other day," he laughed, as we stood in the midst of its incredible complications. "It took me two months to program my last problem and Whirlwind solved it in fifteen minutes."

Programming, he assured me, is not only figuring out the breakdown of the mathematical problem to get it into the binary language of yes-and-no that a computer can understand. A good deal of the time goes into devising tests to make certain that the programming has no mistakes in it. One useful method is to set up a very simple example of the equation you want solved, and work it out by hand. If the computer handles this example and gets the same answer you do, you can be sure you haven't slipped in the programming. If you do slip, the machine may choke on the mistake and stop. Or it may go rambling through and pile up what my guide called "garbage"— a slew of figures that mean nothing. Garbage is not a pleasant sight to a computer engineer. It means that he has got to go clear back to the beginning of his programming and find out where he made his mistake. That may take weeks, too.

It is through programming that computers can be made to behave startlingly like human brains, as, for instance, in making choices and exercising "judgment." They can be programmed, among other things, to select the greater or lesser of two numbers. The numbers themselves can be keyed into the memory so as to initiate sub-programs quite different from one another. The complexity of computer tricks really depends upon the virtuosity of the programmer in working out ways to use the simple yes-no game the computer plays.

Programming instructions to the machine can direct it, for example, to "do this sum in arithmetic. If the result is a negative quantity, look up Instruction 5 and follow it. But if the result is positive, follow Instruction 3. If 3 is chosen, compare the results with those that would follow from 5 and . . ." and so forth, to an almost unlimited set of complications. A common analogy for the working of computers is the Twenty Question game, in which the players track down the identity of an unknown object by asking the referee questions answerable only by "yes" or "no." The analogy is not close, because between questions the human player exercises independent imagination, plays hunches, or uses past experience. To do all this a machine would have to be a super-giant; none such exists. Computers do, however, draw upon limited knowledge stored in their memories, and make decisions based upon the strict logic of what has gone before. Both are activities programmed into them beforehand. A machine can be programmed to play checkers or tick-tack-toe; it is doubtful if one could successfully play Twenty Questions, the yes-and-no habit notwithstanding, unless the programmer had previously entered every conceivable answer in its memory.

Basically, the computer is still a *counter*, and the magnificence of its performance lies rather in the genius of the men behind it than in the machine itself.

18 | OFFICE RESCUE

At the checking counter of your modern grocery store there are two familiar machines—the cash register and the weighing scale. Both are so common in everyday life that you scarcely think of them at all. Both are computers. The scale is an analogue device because it determines weight by balancing an unknown object against a small known weight, automatically swung into a measurable position by the package being weighed. The cash register is a digital computer. It counts. Adding the various items of your purchase, it indicates the amount you owe. New models also subtract that total from the amount you offer in payment, and indicate the change due you.

In a great many country stores the clerk still scribbles the arithmetic out on an empty paper bag. Big stores can't afford the time for this or risk customer disapproval if the boy adds wrong. So they buy machines to do the figuring. Millions of similar paper operations are gradually being mechanized, as the only way to attain speed and accuracy. A vast amount of business, too, is done by automatic vending machines, which wait on the customer as well as take his money. If you buy your cigarettes at one of these, an elementary computer searches for the brand you want and delivers it, *when* you have paid.

The machine understands metal money; some can make change. A similar vending machine sells you parking time at a city curb and computes the length of your stay. It knows when you have stayed too long for your money. Mechanical brain again. Some day take apart one of those "one-armed bandits" found in the Nevada gambling halls. It is a computer all right, programmed to play the public for a sucker but give them just enough breaks to keep them coming back.

A grocery store in Memphis, Tennessee, recently attempted to apply the vending-machine principle to groceries. A section of the store exhibited goods under a glass case. All were numbered. You located what you wanted, then went and bought keys which fitted those particular bins. The keys programmed the food-computing machine and the goods came shooting out, ready to take away. People didn't like this "Keydoozal" system and sales fell off. Food, apparently, is not good fodder for computers. Automation does not belong in retail selling, except where the product is small and standardized.

The businessman, however, is much more interested in mechanizing what goes on behind sales. It is here, in the deep seas of paper, that he seeks rescue by machine. The general purpose of such machines is to remember what is told them and to use the data in working out the complex problems of accounting. Dr. Louis N. Ridenour, well-known atomic scientist and now vice-president of the International Telemeter Corporation, has pointed out that the word *computer* is misleading, since it suggests work done only with figures. He proposes *information machine* instead. For business purposes, at least, this is much more like it. *Data-processing machine* is another term that has the broader meaning. Let us look at a few examples which show how broad the meaning should be.

One of the businessman's worst headaches is his inventory. A department store will carry many thousands of separate items, and must keep close track of its stock so that nothing runs out before it is re-ordered. Schemes are being tried, in the retail business, that tie up the sales slip which the clerk makes out with a recording function which keeps the purchasing department informed at all times. Not long ago, John Plain, a Chicago mail-order house, installed such a system, developed by Remington-Rand. It is called the "Speed Tally." The data-processing unit at the heart of it can keep track, in three separate ways, of 13,000 items. A run of three hours by the "info-machine" (this is my contribution to the jargon) will produce a complete tally of all items. When attending to its regular business of doing the paper work for catalogue customers, the device can handle about 75,000 separate orders per day with the help of ten clerks.

At the heart of the info-machine is a magnetic-drum memory, divided into "listening," storage, and arithmetic sections. As an order comes in, one of the clerks punches out the information—item number, quantity wanted—and this data is picked up by the listening section and transferred to an electronic register. This is a selector, which immediately connects itself with the item's address in the storage section of the drum and reads off the current tally of that item. Both figures are flashed to the arithmetic section and the subtraction is made. The remainder figure goes back to the register and from there returns to drum storage, replacing the old tally for that item. At the same time the transaction is printed out on paper tape in code. The whole operation takes 4/10ths of a second. A close relative of our friend ERMA, you see.

If the purchasing department at John Plain wants to know the tally on any item, the coded tape can supply it to a desk register, or can print it out, merely at the pressing of a read-out button. The entire inventory comes off the tape any time in the same way.

While inventory work is being done in this way in an increasing number of big stores, they must also solve the companion half of the problem, which is keeping track of the goods themselves and knowing where to find them. There may be acres of warehouse space. In non-mechanized establishments, it may take an army of shipping clerks to keep track of it all. The use of automation in stock control is in its infancy, but it is receiving a good deal of thought because the advantages are so great.

A large maker of leather belts has worked out a bin system, combined with belt conveyors and a central info-machine. The order clerks are supplied with keyboards which display, in numbered keys, the entire range of the stock, sizes as well as styles of belt. When an order comes in, the clerk pushes the right button. Down below, the machine hunts up the correct item, connects through to the warehouse, and releases the gate of the right bin. The desired belt drops out, all packaged and ready to go, and is carried to the shipping department, where information as to the customer's address has come in on a register meanwhile. The system is so complete that no time is lost while anyone goes to find anything, either in the office or shipping room. It all comes to hand automatically.

General Electric has gone a long way in automating the enormous flood of paper work that surrounds its order-processing job. In several plants it was found that it took as much as 16 weeks to process a big order. Twelve of them were going into paper work and only four were needed for turning out the goods. A mechanized data system was adopted. The latest figures show that in some cases the 12-week gap could be closed down to 12 hours.

The machines that do this are large and costly; no one yet knows just how they will affect the overhead of a large establishment. But the costs they are aimed at reducing are amazingly high. In a small-tool business which I myself have conducted, I have found that a customer's average *paper* cost of ordering an item selling for $1.25 may be $30 or more. Purchasers are apt not to be interested unless they want to buy enough

units to absorb that high cost. "Industry," says Dr. Joe Harrington, "processes three things: matter, energy, and information." It is an amazing fact that the handling of information by
the present hand-eye-and-brain method can spell the difference
between profit and loss.

A firm's greatest trouble, paperwise, comes in processing a
large number of small orders. "Speed tallying" is all right as far
as it goes, but the best system would be the one which did *all*
paper work at once, in one place. This means that the manufacturing end would be taken care of, too. Only the most talented of info-machines could do this, for in addition to the sales
and accounting end, there would be the secondary flood of
paper which included the shop's job orders, materials tickets,
employe-time, machine-time, and a host of other "little pieces
of paper with marks on them" which industry seems to have
found unavoidable.

At G.E.'s Somersworth, New Hampshire, plant, where electric watt-hour meters are made—the kind you have on the back
of your house—a consistent plan is underway to combine automatic inventory control with cost accounting, shop scheduling,
production, and even *production planning*. Theoretically, this
might include every bit of paper ever to be associated with a
watt-hour meter, from raw material to customer. Details of the
scheme are not yet available, but it will work something like
this: As the automatic machinery turns out the meters, connections on the machines do their own ticketing, via a central
data-processing room. The product is carried by conveyor to a
storage point, where it again comes under the eye of the computer as available for shipment. As orders come in, the machine processes them, keeps all records of the transactions, and
keeps the management posted on inventory. From this collected
data, unit costs are automatically figured and the purchasing
department is alerted to keep up the supply of raw materials.
Financial and tax information can also be integrated with the

rest of the figures, so that the over-all picture of the plant's operation can be seen at a glance. This, though still well in the future, is what General Groves refers to as "consolidated information" supply. It is the sort of thing that executives must have if they are to administer their plants intelligently in the vast flood of demand that is coming.

Speaking of taxes, one enormous burden on all employers is the payroll—not only financially, but from the sheer weight of its paper. A payroll is a complicated exercise in actuarial arithmetic which goes on without relief, year in and year out. It is probably the largest single item of office routine. You cannot simply pay a man what he earned and forget about it. You must first figure what his hourly rate is, and how many days' lost time must be taken off. Then you start with the deductions: withholding for the government income tax and social security (both dependent upon his marital status), state compensation insurance, union dues, withdrawals for special benefits, stock purchases, and many more. When your squad of specialists has done this figuring for the entire company, usually once a week, the pay checks have to be made out and transmitted. Then you do a lot more paper work for state and national governments.

There is no finer opportunity for automatic data-processing than in payroll work, and American business has already gone far toward realizing it. For years IBM card systems have been in use, some of them very complete and including the pay checks themselves. That, however, is only a beginning. The large office computer is now ready to take over, doing the work many times faster. Both the IBM 702 and the Remington-Rand UNIVAC are machines specially gifted in this intricate job. They are able to retain in their memories every possible fact of a man's payroll situation, being re-programmed from day to day as the situation changes. By connection with a punch-card system and a high-speed printer, they can get out the records and the checks in a matter of hours. A considerable number of the larger corporations have rented machines for this purpose (neither UNIVAC nor the IBM 700's are currently sold). Remington-Rand, in fact, offers an *hourly* rental service in their New York headquarters. Companies can send in their payrolls, inventories and other paper problems for servicing at regular intervals. IBM has a similar arrangement.

A field ripe for automation is insurance writing, where the paper work itself is the product sold. The large underwriters have been slow to pick up the info-machine because they already have partial automation in the elaborate punch-card system. But this, after all, involves handling data, in physical form, on cards, and cards have to be sorted and moved from one machine to another, then stored in physical space. The system is open to error at every step where a human hand intervenes.

At the present moment, both Metropolitan Life and Prudential are committed to electronic data-processing. Two years ago, elaborate studies were undertaken by a Prudential team of methods-research men. Today, what is called "policy servicing" is done by means of the IBM giant, "702." The company claims to have made only a very modest beginning with its wonderful new machine, not knowing exactly how much it can do. Already it has cut office machinery in half and rendered obsolete whole acres of files. The 702 will service some three million account records; it will send out ten million premium notices and do the accounting for ten million payments each year. In all, the info-machine and its associated equipment can work at the rate of about 80,000 policies a day.

This is called "modest" because a mechanical brain can do far more—not one yet knows how much more. Some wag has pointed out that it might also figure the boss's expense account, the number of bricks required for that new building project, set up payrolls, keep track of cafeteria costs, and throw in long-range weather forecasts on the side. The truth is, big business is approaching the new day with great caution, for it is not yet

certain how much actual saving will result. The large expense
of making the studies and of scrapping the old system in favor
of the new must be reckoned in. It is probably true that automatic machinery will not realize much real saving until its full
capabilities are exploited.

There is another reason for caution. Nobody knows how long
it will take to train the personnel in the new method, or how
many mistakes will be made by the new combination of machinery and up-graded people. Another wag is responsible for
this story: A large insurance company, using an info-machine,
was annoyed by a mysterious and persistent error. Premium
notices kept coming out of it with a figure of $9000 on them.
The technicians went through the machine tube by tube and
found it all in order. Finally, an office boy approached the chief
engineer. "I know what's the matter," he ventured. "See that
dame over there working the keyboard? You see what a swell
figure she's got?"

"We are not interested in that kind of thing just now, my
boy," the engineer brushed him off.

"No, but watch her," the office boy persisted. "See her lean
over those keys when she punches 'em? Now watch her—her——"

It was true. As the gal poised her beautiful torso over the
keys, one of them lay snugly against the keyboard. Through
the sheer silk of her blouse there was an unexpected point of
contact.

"Works every time," smirked the office boy. "It's in just the
right place to hit the 9000 button."

John Diebold, who is by far the most "sold" expert on office
automation, visualizes an insurance company of the future
where all data concerning the millions of policies will be kept
on magnetic tape in a central computer "bank." This will not
take up space in the company offices, but will occupy its own
building in some part of the city where real estate is cheap. A
clerk at the head office will simply flip a key or two and all

the information on a policy will be printed before him. Diebold points out that in a giant operation like that of Metropolitan, some 15 floors of the great skyscraper in Madison Square are devoted to nothing but files, with battalions of girls shuffling through them all day long.

That prophecy was made in the pre-pioneer days of automation. A system startlingly like the one he imagines is in the works today and will be ready to go about the time our present remarks get into print. The pioneer is not an insurance company but Sylvania Electronic Products, Inc., whose operations are many times more varied than insurance. Dozens of the company's factories, offices and warehouses are spread far and wide over the country. Sylvania is, in the modern pattern, a decentralized business, in which each unit conducts its own affairs and battles its own paper. Management, which heads up near Boston, has a bad time correlating and unifying so many activities. It is a commonwealth almost as sprawling as the British Empire.

Some years ago Sylvania began to worry about its steadily mounting paper costs, its rapidly expanding office force. Paper was becoming a heavy penalty for doing business. It was worried, also, at the difficulty its management was having in unifying the facts and figures from scattered plants in order to make wise decisions. It was obvious that some type of office automation was needed. A well-organized program was initiated. These were the objectives, as stated by the company:

To apply the principles of office automation in all phases of our business where it appears practicable to do so, and to provide management with current up-to-date information, and to permit the application of the latest scientific techniques of management for analysis and control purposes. Though this program is company-wide in nature, it will be designed to permit our decentralized operating units to continue to exercise full executive responsibility at all levels of management and must be an aid to and not a substitute for, these responsibilities.

Thus, they were recognizing General Groves' belief that "the difference between having the facts and not having them makes a poor business manager into a good one and a good one into a super-business manager." The intense competition in the electronics field, in which Sylvania is a leader, made super-management an essential.

Spelled out, the proposition was to build up a complete data-processing and transmission system throughout the company. The heart of it was to be one of the giant info-machines. The UNIVAC, made by General Groves' company, Remington-Rand, was chosen.

Computer techniques, indeed, solved the opening problem, which was to locate the Data-Processing Center where it would serve best. Older methods, by wrangle around a conference table, would surely have put it at the main plant in Massachusetts. The machine, however, digested all of the tangled facts about communications loads and efficient message delivery and named the tiny village of Camillus, not far from Syracuse, New York. And here, in an unassuming little building shaded by Dutch elms in the upper New York State countryside, stands today the world's first concentrated office automation center for a nation-wide business.

The plan, just now beginning to function, is briefly this: Each of the plants, offices and warehouses (there are 51 of them) will be locally automated, so that its figures on costs, inventories, and the like will all be standardized into one form. These figures and facts, while being placed on file in the local offices, will also be committed to punched-paper tape. This tape will be run through a special telegraphic transmitting machine and its coded messages transmitted to a division headquarters office within the plant's own area. Here, the data will be combined with that from all other plants in the region and sent on, still in code, to one of two "switching offices." One of these will be at Salem, Massachusetts, the other at Williamsport, Pennsylvania. From these two, trunk telegraph lines will carry all assembled data to the processing center at Camillus.

To do all this over wires, an arrangement has been made with Western Union to lease approximately 12,000 miles of circuits.

The system, which is admittedly very complicated, is not expected to go into full operation all at once, but will be divided into four phases, to be undertaken one after another as experience is gained. The first phase will involve the info-machine at Camillus in over-all sales accounting and statistical control. The second will concern inventory control and the scheduling of manufacturing operations. The third will advance into untried ground—market research and the forecasting of future business. And the fourth, integrating them all, will be production planning, the golden fleece after which every Ulysses of modern business strives.

As it will work out, the basic "raw" data arriving at the processing center in New York State will be run through the info-machine several times: once for general recording and summarizing, again, under different programming, for sales figures. After that, it can be used for accounting, prophesying, and so on, and for any special aspect of the business on which management may want a quick briefing.

Thus will the modern colossus of business free himself from the collective file drawers and wastebaskets in which he has been floundering and come out upon the level of the empire-builder.

He may not find it as smooth a path upward as some of the pioneers hope. There is still a very deep resistance among business executives to this new-fangled mechanization. The data-processing equipment is so very technical, so very mysterious in its ways, so hard to visualize as a docile employe, that most executives are going at it too slowly. A machine which costs on the average $25,000 a month merely to rent, must be made to serve at top capacity if it is going to be worth its hire. Small, tentative forays into automation are apt to run costs up, not down.

Management, too, is wary of joining the computer boom in its early stages, for it well knows that the changes in equipment and scientific principle will be rapid and costly. Wouldn't it be better to wait till the changes have all been made? One is tempted to ask in retort: Wouldn't it have been better to refrain from using the telephone until everybody had one? How are new ideas to be tested except by use? Conservatism is, or was, a principle of sound business. Today, it is proving to be one of the liabilities. It is dangerous to fall into the error which spelled the doom of the old United States Electric Light Company 70 years ago. The whole company had been built around Hiram Maxim and his inventions in the arc-lamp and dynamo field. Maxim's mind was so fertile that one invention would make another obsolete before the first could be put on the market. The company finally paid Maxim a yearly salary of $20,000 to move to England and never come back. Some of his greatest inventions were made there and he was knighted for them.

Unfortunately, you can't pay computers to stay out of your hair.

Professor Howard Aiken, Harvard's computer pioneer, likes to cook up pungent examples of the limitations of his own brain children. His thesis is that "judgment is the province of man, decisions are the province of machines, so long as the decision is arrived at within the framework of standard policy, which is the sum-total of all past judgment." One of Aiken's favorite examples, illustrating where decision leaves off and judgment begins, concerns a minor company executive who is empowered to decide whether or not to dock the pay of employes who are absent from work. The man delegates his task to a "thinking machine," programmed with the rules about what constitutes a legitimate absence.

When a worker phones in that he won't be on the job because his wife and child have been hurt in an auto accident, the machine decides he gets paid. And when he phones that his grandmother has been killed, the machine refuses to pay. It figures the fellow will wind up in the ball park. But when the absentee sends word that *both* his grandmothers have been killed, the machine cries for help. So does the executive. He takes the case to his boss, who must decide on the basis of the special circumstances. From there on, every combination of relatives killed is a matter of executive decision, in which the machine can't help.

So Sylvania's announced policy is the right one. Automation "must be an aid to and not a substitute for" management's responsibilities.

19 | TODAY AND TOMORROW

The next time you go into the 42nd Street ticket office of American Airlines to buy yourself a plane reservation, notice how the clerk does the paperwork. You ask for a seat on Flight 609 leaving at midnight for Dallas. Almost before the request is out of your mouth, she smiles and says, "I'm sorry, sir. There are no seats available on 609 tonight. But would you like a seat tomorrow morning on 615?" You wonder how she has got the information so fast. The counter is innocent of papers; no schedules are lying about. All you can see is a small object resembling a desk calculator.

You are wondering whether you can afford to wait till tomorrow, when she says, "Oh, a seat has just been given up on the flight you wanted. I will be glad to ticket you."

You are on your way to Texas with the help of a whirling magnetic drum in a second-story room at La Guardia Airport. The drum is the heart of an ultra-modern ticketing machine which American calls the "Reservisor." When you asked the girl on 42nd Street for a seat, she slipped a small metal plate into the "slave-box" in front of her and keyed the number of your requested flight and the figure 1, for one seat. A tenth of a second or so later a red light winked on top of the box, with the words "sold out" under it. Hence she could answer you immediately. But she saw from your face that the flight was important to you, so she left the request set up on the keyboard, thinking that there might be a cancellation from some other part of the city. There was and you got it.

Remember the old way? The row of girls with telephones hunched between shoulder and ear, doodling on desk pads for endless minutes while the party at the other end "went to lunch"? Remember the long lines of people like yourself, surrounded with bags and squalling children, gradually melting away as the big clock on the wall stole the day? That was why American asked The Teleregister Corporation to design a special electronic info-machine for making plane reservations. That, and the fact that constantly increasing plane travel was just about bursting American's operations office at La Guardia with clerks, who dropped telephones to hasten to a huge board on the wall that was keeping tally on the seats available on hundreds of flights. It was that trip to the board, and the necessity of checking to see that the board was right, which kept the ticket lines waiting and spelled steadily mounting costs.

You don't need to go to 42nd Street to make use of the Reservisor in New York. Call at any branch office, or merely telephone Reservations, and the same routine is followed, with the same speed. "REZ" has it all down pat in a jiffy. How does he do it?

Beginning at the slave-set end, when you ask for a seat, the girl chooses a metal "destination" plate that includes your desired flight and pushes it into a slot at the head of the set. This plate, about the size of a wedding invitation, has irregular edges which actuate contacts inside the set and establish certain circuits. The plate, still in view of the clerk, has a number of columns of flights. She pushes a button beneath the column containing your flight. The set has now programmed the question to be asked of REZ. By depressing an entry bar and a

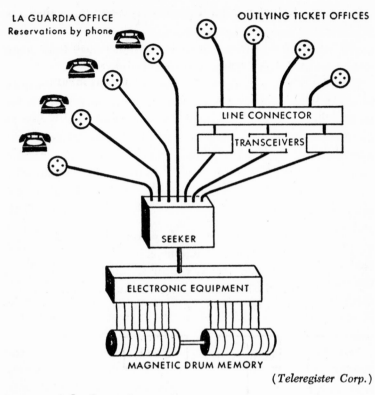

LA GUARDIA OFFICE
Reservations by phone

OUTLYING TICKET OFFICES

LINE CONNECTOR

TRANSCEIVERS

SEEKER

ELECTRONIC EQUIPMENT

MAGNETIC DRUM MEMORY

(*Teleregister Corp.*)

Layout of the Reservisor system

button telling how many seats you want, she causes the request to be transmitted to La Guardia.

Impulses are sent out over a simple telegraph line which has its own automatic switching and can unscramble the many requests for space that are crowding in all the time. At La Guardia your particular set of impulses enters a "transceiver," which is a type of electrical memory, where it is held for its proper turn at the main computer. It is then passed on to the magnetic drum memory and answered. So are all the other requests that pile in. The delay is never more than two or three seconds.

The Reservisor occupies a room no larger than your living room, and consists mostly of electronic tubes and wiring, not unlike ERMA. But REZ is much smaller, for his mind is a trifle dumber than hers. No complicated arithmetic unit is needed, as he only has to subtract numbers up to 70 or so (the total of seats on a plane). Otherwise, much the same routine is followed. It is a matter of looking up the address of the particular flight desired, determining whether or not seats are available, and transmitting a Yes or No out to the agent. If the answer is Yes, then REZ is asked to subtract the newly sold accommodations and chalk up a new remainder.

REZ does have a conscience, however, about making mistakes. All these commercial info-machines have to have. This requires two separate memory drums, running on the same whirling shaft and containing identical information. Both brains work the problem every time. And if they don't come out with

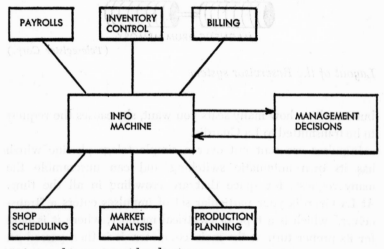

Info-machine as an aid to business

the same answer, REZ knows enough to smell trouble. Like some simple-minded humans, he does not know a little trouble from a lot of trouble, but considers it all serious. So he makes a good job of stirring up the alarm. A red light flashes on the agent's set, a bell rings in the computer room, a piece of paper unfurls from a printer, bringing out the address and all the rest of the information surrounding the error. Like a bright child, he is able to say, "It hurts here, Mummy."

On the printed paper, which is immediately read by the maintenance man on duty, he indicates what part of his anatomy is ailing. Nine times out of ten the trouble is self-healing—a fleck of dust, a "hanging" relay contact—and REZ goes on working, thoughtfully signaling his keeper that he is all right again. The tenth time, when something really fails, he submits to having one brain removed—his form of anesthesia—and the offending organ laid on the operating table for close scrutiny. Meanwhile, with the other brain he continues to sell airplane seats.

This rather fanciful account of a modern office info-machine is by no means intended to belittle the achievement. It took airlines and Teleregister engineers eight years to canvass the problem and work out a satisfactory answer—REZ. When I visited the installation, it had been in service for nearly three years and yet an expert was still hovering over it, bent upon finding ways to improve its operation. A perfectionist attitude, you might say, for the Reservisor has been so successful that American expects to put in several more in other cities. Competing airlines intend to do likewise.

The airline is wholeheartedly pleased with what REZ has done for them. Savings in time and costs, and improvement in customer satisfaction, amply justify the gamble that was originally taken. By meticulous attention to the machine to keep it always in order—REZ is thoroughly tested in the middle of every night—there have been no breakdowns at all. Nor has American stirred up a labor problem. Thirty-two men and women "lost" their jobs when REZ took over, but the company ended that year by hiring 18 more, in addition to transferring the 32 to better work. The reservations business is rising steadily, and while they don't hire people any more to run back and forth to the big wall chart with slips of paper, nor employ others to chase out the unavoidable human mistakes, they do hire continually to fill new posts in the ticketing offices. In passing, it might be noted that not one of REZ's five million solder connections was done by machine. Such expert work never can be.

It won't be long now before you meet automatic ticketing in all big cities on all kinds of transportation. People have worn so many holes in railroad- and bus-station floors waiting for

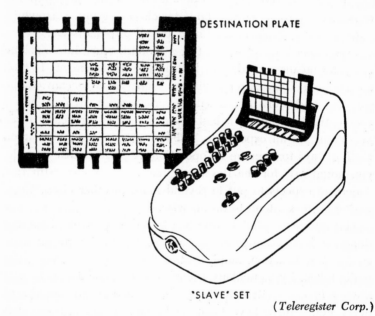

DESTINATION PLATE

'SLAVE' SET

(*Teleregister Corp.*)

REZ's *programming units*

service that the virtues of the new info-machines as friends of
the once-damned public are being seriously investigated. At
the Grand Central Station in New York you get a service somewhat similar to that at the airline. When you can buy theater
tickets the same way, that will be the day!

The railroads, it is to be noted, have not been asleep to automatic operation. In fact, their adoption of automatic signaling
took place so long ago that you have grown up with it. This is
not quite automation, but it does borrow an important feature
from it—the fail-safe principle. On the single-track roads that
crisscross the nation, it is too dangerous to run high-speed
trains without knowing where they are at every instant. The
modern dispatcher, who is completely in charge of traffic in a
division some hundreds of miles wide, sits at an automatic
board watching little lights that reveal where each train is.
Without getting up, he manipulates the signals by push-button
control and gets through to the engine cabs with his orders,
too. The whole system is a matter of intercommunication, but
the safety factor, which is paramount, is left to natural laws.
Signals are so arranged that if any part of the man-made system
fails, the lights go red and the semaphore arms swing to the
Stop position. The mere *absence* of electrical impulses in the
signal lines leaves the road open for gravity, which promptly
hoists the semaphores and trips the green-light relays to red.
This is "fail-safe."

Railroading is by nature a cumbersome, conservative business. Yet all this talk about computers and automation has not
missed them. There is a very stiff problem in the handling of
freight that they would be glad to have automation take over.
As you may know, freight cars are pooled in huge siding areas
called "classification yards," dotted over the country. Here, cars
from the four points of the compass continually arrive, are
shunted and shuffled day and night, and made up into new
trains, each one headed toward a general destination. These

yards have a profile like the outline of a sleeping girl. Near one end there is a "hump." Cars are pushed to it by locomotives, then freed and allowed to coast downgrade toward the particular sidetrack that contains the train they are joining up with. High above the racket a tower man controls all this by automatic switching. At night the yard must be lit up like a ball park, for every car must go down the grade at just the right speed to "kiss" its train but not beat it up.

The tower man has at his fingertips a series of "track retarders"—friction devices on the rails that he can operate by push button. If he thinks a car is going too fast, he can slow it down. There is nothing he can do to hurry it up, except send a locomotive after it. After dark, his judgment is often impeded by shadows, rain, snow, and highly variable track conditions. Worse, he can only estimate the liveliness of a particular car by consulting its lading sheet. Manipulating it is a matter of guesswork and long experience. Right now, as you read this, $200,000,000 is lost every year because cars slam into each other and wreck the freight inside them. As an average car must pass through six classification yards in crossing the country, its jeopardy is considerable.

Stanford Research Institute, creators of ERMA, are in the midst of a technical study for the Southern Pacific Railroad, to see if the whole thing can't be handled by a data-processing device. SP has four yards in its huge system. It believes that electronic car-handling would save $1000 a day in each yard.

The idea—and it is only that now—is to place upon the track near the hump a set of sensing elements that will determine the exact weight of the car. Elsewhere, detectors will establish the slipperiness of the tracks below. Further data tells where the car is going and how fast the engine has started it coasting off the hump. A computer, programmed to combine all these factors, will decide just how fast the car must be rolling at the top of the grade in order to arrive safely, and gently, at the end of its train. The yard engine, then, need only deliver all cars to the hump at the same speed, slightly greater than needed. Through retarders on all sidings, the machine will slow down each car to the exact speed required for it to make its journey.

Traffic control in America is, of course, a tremendous and steadily worsening problem, not only on the railroads but in every city and at every airport. In comparison with these, the freight-yard operation is only an elementary example. The same computer elements, however, can solve all of them, because mechanical brains have the ability to render instant decisions. It is not hard to believe that a robot could take over from the typical cop at a busy intersection at rush hour and do a better job. It would be no criticism of the police, who are admittedly desperate.

An automatic traffic-control system has actually been tried out on an arterial highway in Van Nuys, California. For eleven miles electronic eyes on traffic poles view the streams of cars on the main highway and on cross streets. The data, fed to an info-machine, changes the lights in such a way that the long-sought justice on the highways is achieved. Miles of cars do not pile up when one man rolls out of a side street; people no longer have to wait for red lights that favor empty alleys. Pedestrians get their chance, too, but cannot halt everything at will by pushing a button. The whole system is keyed to unsnarl traffic. A computer is the only kind of brain that can do it.

At the airports it is not convenience that dictates the traffic pattern, but downright saving of lives. The men in the control tower of a big airport like La Guardia have a tremendous job, generally divided into two parts. First, there is a mass of routine operation—getting planes off, interweaving them successfully with ships coming in. Then there is the constantly menacing problem of the emergency—as when a plane misses a landing and upsets the pattern, or in landing, finds a small plane on the runway. Or, in bad weather, when the port is just on the verge of being closed in. The danger arises because the routine work is so complicated that a very slight variation may throw everything into a tangle.

A system has been proposed—it is in the works—for turning all routine traffic control over to an info-machine. This robot would be operated by signals from the various planes, each of which would communicate to it the essential facts of its position and desired maneuvers, *continuously*. The computer would "think over" the situation, instant by instant, and issue a steady stream of orders to all planes at once, standing at the shoulder of every pilot until he had safely left the pattern.

Tower personnel, of course, could override the machine at any instant merely by pushing an Out button, and the robot would itself signify to the pilots that it was relinquishing control. Such a system has the important advantage that it can work out, mathematically, the safest and most economical method of handling any number of planes, without making errors in judgment. The machine would not arrive at its solution by guesswork, but would investigate thousands of possible landing and take-off maneuvers and fix upon the best one, second by second.

It is in this kind of automatic control that the public will first feel the impact of automation. Part of that feeling will be in the pocketbook, too, for a machine that takes over routine can always show savings.

Speaking of pocketbooks, we should not miss an idea of John Diebold's for automating the Stock Exchange. Here we have a paper operation which is really ripe for modernization. The brokers themselves rarely go onto the Floor of the Exchange. Specialists do that, milling and shouting their bids and button-holing buyers and sellers in a mad rush to get there first. It is like a thousand auctions going on at once in the same house.

What Diebold suggests is that the Floor itself be replaced by

an info-machine, demurely installed in a vault in some downtown New York basement. The machine's memory will contain
all of the current data on stock prices, bid-and-asked figures,
shares sold, ex-dividend data, and so forth. Branch circuits will
run to each brokerage office. All the broker has to do is dial or
punch out on a keyboard a message that he wants to buy or sell
a certain stock. Instantly, the computer will reply with a quo-
tation. An Execute button will complete the transaction. The
desk console in each office will print out a continuous list of
Exchange dealings, and at the end of the day a high-speed
printer will provide a detailed statement of the business the
office has done, showing what its obligations are.

Such a system would decimate the work of the Exchange.
The computer might even have trunk lines to other cities, so
that the whole country could participate. There is only one
trouble: the Stock Exchange isn't likely to go for automation.
The personal touch is too important. However, Diebold has
predicted correctly more than once. Perhaps the Exchange will
permit itself to be modernized again, as it once was by a
young man whose name subsequently turned out to be Thomas
Edison. It was he who invented the stock ticker.

If Edison were alive today, perhaps he could sell automation
in Wall Street where others could not. At any rate, he would
be the first to exult over a bronze plaque set in the side of an
old brick building at the General Electric plant in Schenectady.
The lettering tells you that it was here, in Building 10, that
Edison first began his electrical-manufacturing work. Building
10, now, is the company's most advanced hatchery for automation.

It would be a pity to close this sampling chapter on the odds
and ends of computer automation without mentioning an ingenious idea of certain engineers of the Datamatic Company,
a lively contender in the info-machine field. Their thought is
that almost everyone, at one time or another, has been in some

kind of a jam with a magazine subscription department. Miss Smith of New Jersey, who began this book, is one. I'm another. I have no doubt that the present reader is a third. There always seems to be something the matter with a magazine subscription. Either the journal comes late or not at all; either it stops coming before the subscription has run out or it keeps on coming indefinitely, for free. A man I know has been getting three copies of the *Saturday Evening Post* for years. All he tried to do was to give it to his mother for Christmas. She thought it would be more fun for him than for her, so she tried to change the subscription. When it came to him he protested and explained. The information merely brought him an extra copy each week. Two protests brought two extra ones. And you know what happens when you change your address. . . .

The publishers do not like this, either, but their misfortune is that most subscriptions come in around Christmas, making an enormous clerical load that can only be met by hiring hundreds of temporary (and not too well-trained) girls to battle the paper deluge. My friends at Datamatic had this answer: just let a computer do it.

Into the computer's memory goes the subscription file. By having a few highly competent people in charge of it, there would be little danger of an error originating at the start of a subscription, even at Christmas. Anyway, the machine would print back each new name and address and the subscription facts for the operator to double-check. Only when it was solidly verified would she punch the O.K. button. From then on, this unnamed mechanical genius would do the work.

For instance, it would get out the weekly or monthly mailing list, by feeding directly into an associated high-speed printer similar to ERMA's. Then, if a subscriber wrote in to change his address while he went on vacation, the operator would only have to feed in the new facts, verify them, and let the robot see to it that you got your copies in the woods or wherever you happened to be, till time to come home. You would find the magazine waiting on your doorstep.

Mistakes such as multiple copies would be impossible. Nor would a gift subscription come to you if you tried to send it to someone else. The funny part is that some subscribers don't seem to know their own names or where they live. Often they give wrong addresses, or write so illegibly that clerks can't understand them. This would not faze our info-machine at all. Working hand in hand with its operator, it would explore the records, eliminating, one after another, the subscribers of similar name who did not live in the right town, on the right streets, or have the right initials.

I am a magazine subscriber myself, and this invention is hereby recommended to the publishers, in all seriousness. Undoubtedly, the machine will be adorned with initials that just happen to spell out a name. I will solve that one, too. Call the machine MAGGIE, which, of course, will stand for Magazine Garbled Information Eliminator.

20 | MATHEMATICS ON WINGS

Although there are hundreds of special-purpose info-machines in service, the majestic sweep of their talents shows up best in the large general-purpose "brains" used for scientific research. There are many ways in which a scientific problem differs from those of business. Dr. Mina Rees, of Hunter College in New York, puts it clearly: "A scientific problem usually involves a great deal of computation on relatively small amounts of data. Many business problems, on the other hand, and many military and operational problems as well, are characterized by large amounts of data and relatively small amounts of computation."

The general-purpose machine, then, is more properly called a computer, though it can do far more than merely solve equations. As it would be quite impossible to detail the theory of a big computer's operation here—there are plenty of technical articles on the subject—our best plan will be to visit a few and pick up what we can as we watch them work.

My own first contact with computers was in the Electrical Engineering Laboratory at M.I.T., during the twenties and thirties. Dr. Van Bush was then head of the department. With an assistant, Fred Dellenbaugh, and the close co-operation of many others, he was piling into the problem of mechanical computation. I had just invented my little "harmonic analyzer" for measuring harmonics in alternating-current circuits, and was an interested if mystified onlooker.

Bush's first differential analyzer, or analogue computer, was a laboratory table covered with shafts and gears, disks and pulleys, turned by a small motor. He was not interested in a single type of calculation, as I had been, but in solving differential equations of as many types as possible. A differential equation is one in which variable quantities are linked in some kind of team play with the main variable, x, but in which the solution (or many solutions) is found by reducing the variables to infinitesimally small quantities and then "integrating" them—that is, adding up an infinite number of the tiny fragments to get an answer. Sir Isaac Newton discovered the method of differentials and integrals which he called "Fluxions." This mathematical tool has since been named "the calculus," from the Latin *calculi*, meaning "pebbles," which were once used in counting. The calculus has become indispensable in solving the problems of science. It is actually a method of approximation.

If you wanted to find out how fast a baseball would hit the ground if dropped off the 500-foot Washington Monument, you could prepare a formula, or differential equation, expressing how far and how fast the body would fall in an infinitesimally short time. It would include the distance, the acceleration due to gravity, and the time of falling through that distance, and would be of the mathematical form $v = \dfrac{ds}{dt}$. The term s expresses distance and in turn involves acceleration, which, at any instant, can be symbolized by $a = \dfrac{d^2s}{dt^2}$. By combining and integrating these expressions, you obtain the general formula for a falling body, $v = \sqrt{2gs}$, where g is the known acceleration of gravity, about 32.2 feet per second per second. Your baseball would thus hit the ground at a speed of nearly 180 feet per second, or two miles a minute.

Plain algebra won't help in this case, except in the form of infinitesimals. The details of integrating we won't go into here. Newton's brilliant discovery was that you could extend algebraic methods to cases where all the elements in a problem were varying, by this use of tiny quantities summed up.

Countless technical problems must be solved in this way: the behavior of electric circuits, of steam engines and turbines, of bridges under load, of bullets, of the flow of fluids in pipes, of the weather; and innumerable manufacturing problems, such as the design of steel-mill motors or the layout and operation of telephone circuits to accommodate the most subscribers with the least equipment. There is no branch of technology which does not lean heavily on the calculus. It is a basic language which scientists speak as often as they do English. The operations, however, may be tedious and lengthy, and it may be difficult when problems involve many variables intricately related.

Bush felt that a differential calculator was essential in speeding up the hack work of mathematics. His machine was able to solve differential equations because its mechanical parts could be adjusted to interact with each other precisely as the elements in an equation did. As he went on into the thirties, he found that mechanical analogues were too inaccurate and too slow. In his later models nothing moved but electrons.

Bush's brilliant work started the ball rolling. Numerous analyzers were invented in the next few years. Then, about the time of the outbreak of World War II, Dr. John W. Mauchley, of the U.S. Bureau of Standards, proposed a calculator in which the solutions of complicated calculus problems would be done by *counting*. His suggestion was that vacuum tubes be used, in somewhat the same way that beads are used in the Chinese abacus. It was his belief that practically any differential problem, if broken down into fine enough detail, could be handled by simple addition and subtraction. The same thing could be done by hand with nothing more than a pencil, but would take years or centuries. Vacuum tubes, however, with their speeding electrons, should bring the time down within reason.

Mauchley and J. P. Eckert, Jr., of the University of Pennsylvania, tackled the problem and the result was ENIAC, a huge roomful of 18,000 vacuum tubes, relays, wires, punch-card machines, generators, motors, transformers and a substantial air-conditioning system to keep the whole thing from melting in its own heat. ENIAC (Electronic Numerical Integrator and Calculator), as we have already mentioned, got Army Ordnance off the hook by calculating their firing tables in a matter of hours. The day I visited the huge machine it was programmed for an exhibition stunt, calculating a table of cubes by the formula, $y = x^3$. The room was lined with panels mounting a vast number of little neon lamps that winked red as they counted. There were acres of them. We were invited to watch the progress of the problem as ENIAC solved it.

When the engineer in charge cried "Now!", an assistant threw a switch. There was a brief dash of color, as if someone had swept a pink spotlight around the room. We hurried across to the output board and there it was, the table of cubes from 1 to 100, all done. ENIAC could do 5000 additions per second. It was in code, of course, and unintelligible to us, but that was soon fixed. An attendant started an IBM printing machine, and the cube table, in common figures, began to emerge. Try working up a cube table with pencil and paper. It will take you a good many hours.

ENIAC, once it was "debugged," was shipped off to the Army and has been working steadily for them ever since. It was the grandfather of UNIVAC, the Remington-Rand wizard calculator, which Mauchley also worked out. UNIVAC came into an intense public spotlight when, on the night of the election of 1952, it predicted a landslide for Eisenhower. We all remember the hasty apologies made over the air for UNIVAC's "mistake," and how right the computer turned out to have been, hours later. Even at that early stage, the mechanical "brain" was out-guessing the smartest political dopesters.

Mauchley, of course, had not been alone in this pioneer venture with ENIAC. Dr. Claude Shannon, of the Bell Telephone Laboratories, had been studying the calculating problem for some time, and probably deserves as much credit as anyone for originating the digital method or binary counting system, on which these new computers were to work. It was Shannon who cut to the root of the problem when he said, "A digital computer must be instructed in words of one micro-syllable." We shall meet him again presently.

Almost at the same time as Mauchley, Commander Howard Aiken was creating a huge scientific computer at Harvard. Commander Aiken had been lent by the Navy to Harvard's Computation Laboratory, to develop a machine for solving naval gunnery problems. IBM had offered to finance it. The work at Harvard was pushed at top speed; soon after war began, this early giant emerged briefly, then disappeared into a shroud of secrecy, commandeered by the military. MARK I, it was called. It had 700,000 parts, 3000 of them electric relays, more gears than all the watches in Cambridge, wire enough to —go a long way. Though it covered one whole side of a big laboratory room, one five-horsepower motor made it go.

MARK I was not an electronic computer but a straight electro-magnetic relay machine. Relays are simply switches operated by the pull of an electromagnet. There are three of them in your car's generator circuit, which is a primitive type of auto-matic calculator. Since there is actual physical motion in a relay "armature," it takes time to work. This made the MARK I very slow—a matter of minutes or hours for the solution of a com-plex problem, rather than of seconds. But MARK possessed great tenacity, was simple, easily serviced, and fairly easy

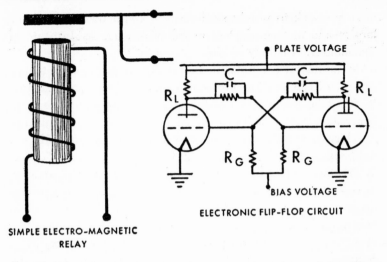

PLATE VOLTAGE

R_L C C R_L

R_G R_G

BIAS VOLTAGE

ELECTRONIC FLIP-FLOP CIRCUIT

SIMPLE ELECTRO-MAGNETIC
RELAY

to program. It was a good beginner. Aiken has since built
MARK II and MARK III, the last fully electronic. Today, if you
visited him, he would show you I and III, working side by side
in a neat, orderly room with lots of floor space and a crew of
some half dozen Ph.D.'s quietly hovering over desks nearby.
MARK II is not there now.

The MARK's were the prototypes of the now-famous IBM
701 and 702, which have retained their outward neatness but
have become incredibly complicated inside. These are both
electronic machines. A few hours in an IBM factory will quickly
prove how complicated they are, and will give foundation for
Dean Wooldridge's remark that computer building may become
America's largest industry. It takes hundreds of skilled factory
workers and technicians at least a month to construct one of
these giants, and sales engineers many more to determine how
a purchaser can best use the monster. Commander Aiken once
ruefully remarked, "There has never been a labor-saving invention yet. Every time a new gadget is thought up it only makes
more work for more people."

To go back to purely mathematical computers. One of the largest and most modern is at the Massachusetts Institute of Technology. It is very sensibly named "Whirlwind." It is by all odds the fastest computer in the world (it may not be tomorrow), and can swallow problems of a complexity so great that it often takes months of a mathematician's time to get the problem ready. A few hours usually suffices to solve the problems.

Whirlwind went into action in Cambridge late in 1951, and has been constantly reworked and improved since. As a "child," Whirlwind could remember, act upon, and deliver information at the rate of 2000 times a second, and was thereby suited to dealing with problems where near-instant decision is needed. Such a problem, as we have seen, would be the routine handling of airplane traffic-control patterns, where the initial conditions requiring solution do not remain fixed, but are constantly changing. Many military problems of control need this kind of speed. Whirlwind was undertaken because M.I.T. has been very close to the continental defense project. In fact, Whirlwind is the grandfather of SAGE, the fantastic computer system recently unveiled for detecting and shooting down enemy planes.

The incredible speed of the modern computing machine has an amusing sidelight. According to Dr. Louis N. Ridenour, digital computers of today are presumed to be about 20 times *too slow* to give satisfactory solutions to many "real time" problems, such as the airport-traffic job. Analogue machines, on the other hand, produce continuous solutions without any delay at all. But the analogues are not accurate enough, and become too complicated as the mathematical demands become heavier. This is why every effort is being made today to speed up the digital computer to astronomical accomplishments.

Whirlwind's speed derives from the fact that in dealing with numbers, it does not take one digit after another and work on it. It takes them all at once. Its designers realized that a magnetic drum, such as those in ERMA and REZ, was not nearly fast enough. These computers have to wait for information to unreel, so that assembling it takes time. Whirlwind's inventors needed an action system definitely divorced from time. They came very close to achieving it with the so-called "electrostatic" type of memory, using vacuum tubes much like television tubes. By modulating the strength of a beam of electrons sweeping around inside the tube, spots of information could be placed on the screen of the tube at incredible speed. A 16-digit number (in binary code) could be read into or out of the machine's memory in 25-millionths of a second.

Unlike the TV picture tube, this memory did not fade away. The spots were constantly refreshed by another electron beam, working behind the "writer" all the time. This description I have put in the past tense because the electrostatic memory was abandoned as too slow and uncertain about three years ago. A still faster, virtually instantaneous memory called "magnetic core storage" was substituted. The brilliant physicist who invented it, Dr. Jay W. Forrester, is at present presiding over the mysterious Lincoln Laboratory of M.I.T. at Bedford, Massachusetts. In order to understand Whirlwind's breathtaking speed, we must go there for a moment.

Lincoln is one of the most secret scientific entities in the country. No outsider visits it without complete supervision; its miles of corridors and laboratories and offices are largely out of bounds. The laboratory building, bristling with radars, is not even named over the portico. For at Lincoln a good deal of the country's major defense is being worked out.

You have come there to see Forrester's magnetic core memory, and that is all you will see. Fortunately it is not secret. Practically blindfolded, you are led to a big basement room, where you realize instantly that you are in the world of advanced experiment. Here is a low-ceiled, close-packed space, as

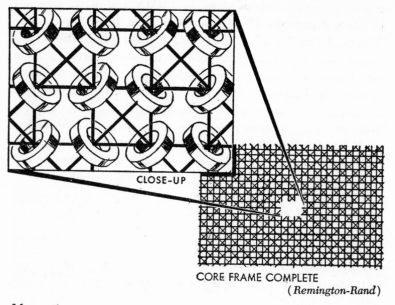

CLOSE-UP

CORE FRAME COMPLETE
(*Remington-Rand*)

Magnetic core memory

completely overrun with working machinery as a subway station with people at quitting time. MTC, the Memory Test Computer designed to run tests on the magnetic core device, is
sprawled everywhere. Rows and rows of panels, all with wires
draped over, across, and under them. More rows of sweating
vacuum tubes, cables snaking across the floor, men in jujitsu
positions fixing, testing, repairing; men sitting at what might
be the console; men standing, reading instruments; men leaning
over, reading magnetic tape; men on tiptoe, studying a skipping
little green spot on a kind of television screen. And behind
them an incessant cacophony of bleeps and peeps, squeaks,
squawks, titters, and rumbles. Bops here, chatters there, bits of
technical conversation just as intelligible; once in a while a
Valkyrie siren whooping briefly and sinking into the steady

drum and hum of electrical machinery which is the pedal point of the whole thing.

In back, stepping over, and under, and around wires and down long, thin alleys between glowing electron tubes that might easily kill you, lies the path to the magnetic cores. This at last is the heart of a giant computer, a heart laid wide open, aorta, ventricles, and all. It is not very large or very impressive, this new memory device. It resembles a stack of small fly screens, out of the sides of which bleed hundreds of little colored wires.

The magnetic core memory consists of two banks of these screen-like frames, each frame crossed by evenly spaced wires in four directions. At every intersection within the frame there is a tiny black ring, about as big as the head of a burnt match. The ring embraces all four wires at once. On each frame there are 1024 of them; in the whole unit some 20,000. Every ring has been painstakingly threaded on the four wires by hand.

Electric pulses can pass through a ring on any of the four wires in either direction. An impulse traveling in one direction magnetizes a ring (which is made of a compound of insulating material and iron oxide) with a certain polarity, thus setting up one of the two yes-no conditions required by the binary system. An impulse in the other direction magnetizes it oppositely. Either polarity will remain till it is rubbed out by a current sent to do this. To read out a "bit" of information, an exploratory impulse is sent through one of the wires, too weak to destroy the ring's magnetic pole. The effect upon the impulse is enough to detect whether a "yes" or a "no" is stored there. The polarity discovered tells which of the two bits it is.

"That's all there is to it," said my guide, without cracking a smile.

The computer has a "muscle" which beats out a rhythm of impulses at the rate of one every millionth of a second. They don't get in each other's way because each one only lasts one-ten-millionth of a second. A single pulse is enough to carry one bit of information anywhere in the machine desired. Some of the routines the machine goes through take much longer, some as much as eight millionths of a second. Tossed aside to a crawling magnetic drum, various information-passengers on this rapid-transit system "sit in the waiting room" between impulse trains. They may have to wait as long as 67 millionths of a second sometimes—enough to go get a sandwich and a cup of coffee.

Fun aside, Dr. Forrester's invention is changing the whole aspect of mathematical computers. With his feet on his table as I talked to him, he seemed unaware of it and in no hurry at all. Modestly, he would tell you that there is still much to be done to improve the core memory. Tall, gangling, incredibly keen, he would be the first to admit that the memory, as we see it today, is only a way station on the road stretching on toward unexplored new countries of knowledge. IBM has already picked up the magnetic-core idea for its new 702's, and has on the fire a machine to string tens of thousands of period-sized rings on four wires without ruining the eyes of a roomful of girls.

The core memory is fast because nothing turns or moves except electrons and the atoms of iron in the little rings. However, bits of iron do have mass and it takes time to orient them when they are held together in solid form. The ideal—and it has been soberly proposed—is to find a way to make the atom itself act as a memory. An atomic memory is conceivable; it could do all that the biggest computer could need done on the head of a pin. Will the mechanical mathematician of the future, then, be called Pinhead? Quite a lot of water must flow under the bridge before we shall know. The problem of using a memory is the means of getting information in and out of it. How do you obtain reports from *one atom at a time*, when it is only a millionth of a millionth of an inch in diameter?

Whirlwind, when I saw it, or rather, walked through it, was as neat as MTC was jumbled. You are always taken through these machines by a guide, and this one was a pleasant young mathematician named Jack. He had a reel of magnetic tape in his hand and gave it to a Negro programmer who was sitting at the console. Jack explained that they'd had a little trouble with certain computations lately, so he had reeled up some special instructions to test the machine. A hyperbolic function table, he said it was. We chatted a minute at the console, where some half dozen men were touching buttons and looking at lights. The machine was going full blast but seemed to have some spare corners in it for Jack's problem. He was apologetic about it; he didn't blame the computer, but assumed that he had made a mistake in programming the problem that had gone wrong. He'd been collecting nothing but garbage the past few days.

I watched the Negro engineer thread on Jack's tape. He pressed a button and the tape disappeared—20 feet of it swallowed up in a couple of seconds. "Let's see how I came out," Jack said.

"Already?"

We crossed to a large typewriter in a corner, which was banging away by itself, turning out a huge sheet of figures. As we arrived it stopped, and Jack tore some of the paper out.

"Right there," he said, indicating a brace of figures. "I goofed it. I'll have to pull that program apart and see what's wrong."

It would take a good many days to do that, I learned. This programming in higher mathematics is strictly graduate stuff. Longer, by far, than that test had taken. Two minutes, perhaps, would have covered the test, including a complete printing of some hundreds of figures.

Whirlwind is quite spacious. A good-sized night club would

be needed to furnish the floor space. However, one gets the impression, rather, of visiting the stacks of a big library. Steel cabinets are lined up in long rows, with convenient bays between. The familiar stepladders are there in quantity, in case the service crew needs to do something up near the ceiling. One thing about all these giants: they are composed mainly of what the electronics people call "standard hardware." Small steel boxes that pull out of the panels, contain groups of tubes and associated elements, very like a radio set. There are thousands of these. While we were there a maintenance man pulled one out and replaced it. The computer went on chattering, as a patient does while the doctor binds up a cut finger. This maintenance job was rather special, I was told. Whirlwind monitors its own tubes and signals the desk when it is time to change them.

Jack was a trifle apologetic about the size of Whirlwind. It could be done, he said, in far less space, especially if the thousands of tubes were replaced by pea-sized transistors. Transistors would do for the computer pretty much what vacuum tubes do now, with enormous saving of space. Transistors do not light up and get hot, as tubes do. Hence the bulky refrigeration plant of the present giant could be eliminated. Transistors are ready for the job, but transistor *manufacture* is not. They are still expensive because they are under development. Computers will all have them in the future, no doubt.

As we came back to the control console, a group was clustered around a circular screen high up on the board that looked like an overgrown television tube. It was just that. Words were appearing on it, words and figures, in large, legible type. They would stay for a few seconds and then be replaced. Nearby was a movie camera, clicking away as it watched the screen. Jack explained. This was one of Whirlwind's output systems at work—one of many. For fast reading and for recording on film that can be projected on a screen, the TV unit is used. For tabulating many figures for future study, the automatic printer is better. Magnetic tape can be substituted, if permanent storage in coded form is desired. The TV unit is especially useful for a machine so heavily jammed with work. An outsider can get quick answers, photograph them and leave with his film without bothering any of the permanent-storage devices.

"Outsiders?" I questioned him. "How often would a man want to come in off the street to compute a few stray problems on his way downtown to work?"

"Oftener than you'd think," Jack replied. "Whirlwind is quite popular. And by the way"—he looked at his watch—"we've got to get out of here. The Navy comes on at four." The Navy, it seemed, did classified work from four to midnight and the Air Force took its turn in the daytime from eight to four. M.I.T. got what was left, the graveyard shift. I had been lucky. USAF had finished early that afternoon. Whirlwind, it seemed, *could* accommodate all three at once and keep its records straight, too. But the military doesn't work that way. It prefers to figure things out alone, each branch in its own little water-tight compartment. Computer practice for M.I.T. students is rugged. They do all their work between midnight and dawn.

21 | DO THEY THINK?

A good many technical people get mad when you call a computer a "giant brain." They insist that it does only what thinking humans have thought up for it to do in advance. Lady Lovelace, Lord Byron's daughter, is reported to have said of Babbage's difference engine, "It has no pretensions whatever to originate anything. It can do whatever we know how to order it to perform." Professor M. V. Wilkes, Cambridge University's computer specialist, said more recently, "I suspect that to many people thinking means something which can be done by a human being, or possibly by an animal, but not by a machine."

Dr. Joe Harrington barks, "Can machines think? No! Not if thinking means to reason. A computer has less brains than a worm, which is known to be among the lowest forms of life."

The *pro's* are much more vociferous. Edmund Berkeley states categorically, "A machine can handle information; it can calculate, conclude and choose; it can perform reasonable operations with information. A machine, therefore, can think." Wilkes himself admits that a machine that can simulate human behavior, and therefore pass itself off as a human being, might be said to think. Norbert Wiener, of M.I.T., envisions a machine which can learn and will "in no way be obliged to make such decisions

234

as we should have made, or will be acceptable to us." Evidently, he thinks they can think.

There is a story of a computer programmer who, just for a lark, spent days setting up the machine to destroy itself, then stood by grinning as it dutifully proceeded to commit suicide. If that machine could have thought, would it not have circumvented him? But then there is another story, telling of a young genius who designed a machine to play tick-tack-toe with him, resolving to build it so cleverly that it would always beat him. It always did, and this he thought peculiar, because certain moves by the opening player will invariably draw the game. Puzzled, this young man took his robot apart and found that it had been cheating him.

Dr. A. L. Samuel, an electronics expert, remarks somewhat ruefully, "Regardless of what one calls the work of the digital computer, the unfortunate fact remains that more rather than less human thinking is required to solve a problem using a present-day machine." This is because machines have no discretion. Every possible contingency must be thought through beforehand if the machine is to behave. But what about the machine that can learn? Many of them can. Is it not possible, as Wiener implies, that it could learn something we don't know?

To me the controversy boils down to a definition of the word *think*. There is no field in all physiology that is less explored than that of the human brain. Practically all that is known is that the brain contains some ten billion tiny cells called "neurons." Apparently, these are elementary memory units, capable of storing the same kind of information "bits" that a machine can store. A completely materialistic view suggests that they, with the help of an extraordinary network of nerve-communication lines, is all there is to the brain, and that somehow the combination can originate thought as well as perform routine duties with it. Possibly the best differentiation between man and machine is a quantitative one. The brain has roughly a

million times as many components as the best computer. On
the other hand, the difference may lie in a spiritual factor, em-
braced by religion. At any rate, a machine cannot exercise free
will or originate anything—not yet. Whether it ever will is still
an open argument.

Nevertheless, an information machine can already do a lot
of surprising things. A good many advanced experimenters are
trying to see just how far it can be pushed toward undeniable
thought. "Computers," Samuel points out, "make possible a
form of numerical experimentation which has never before
been exploited. Problems can be tackled which have such overwhelming detail that nobody has even attempted them." We
have seen the beginning of work along these lines: prediction
of the weather by using vast quantities of data; the simplification of actuarial work for insurance companies; the making of
executive decisions from facts no one would have time to write
up by present methods.

These, however, are routine tasks which require thinking of
a very low order. Let us see what happens when we go beyond
mere codification. Dr. Claude E. Shannon, the mathematical
genius employed by the Bell Telephone Laboratories, is largely
responsible for the "Information Theory" which has constituted
the scientific breakthrough in automation in the past ten years.
He is also a leader in computer design, and a persistent searcher
for methods of making machines more intelligent. The work
is based on the fact that information and its communication
are the central mathematical entities upon which all data-
processing machines depend. Shannon's great contribution,
based on the brilliant work of Norbert Wiener in cybernetics
(the science of control mechanisms), was to build up a mathematical method of treating information as a commodity, much
as if it were a fluid moving through a pipe. Information move-
ments, he established, obey the laws of thermodynamics, which
have been understood for a century.

If you consider it closely, information turns out to be a ruling factor in our lives. Day-to-day living is conducted very largely on material that is either stored in our memories or apprehended by our senses. Very little purely original thought is used at a time of action; most of our information comes, or has come, from outside. The human being possesses an amazing information system, embodying the brain, the nerve channels, the muscles, employing thousands of feedback signals which constantly compare a desired performance with an actual one. On this basis, how far can we go towards devising a mechanical replica of ourselves? To date, not very far. Compared to the brain, the machine is a pauper in data-storage facilities, and it is capable of only the most elementary capture and use of information. However, Shannon's discovery opens the way to a series of machines which act on the same principles as the human mind.

The preoccupation of men like Shannon, Wiener, Dr. J. von Neumann and a host of others, is with computing devices that do *non-numerical* work: that is, machines that "go on from there" after all the figures are in. These researchers have wanted to see, for example, whether the act of *learning* could be mastered by hardware; whether inanimate devices could exercise judgment, make choices, originate ideas, could play games intelligently. And at the farthest limit of possibility, whether, at least on paper, they could *reproduce themselves.* In other words, are we really certain that a machine can do only what its programmer wills it to do?

There are a number of machines in existence already which have reached some of these goals. The simplest type is the computer which understands logic. It may be a trifle snide to say so, but many people are quite divorced from logic. Their brains do not normally have an appreciation of *sequitur*—of the significance of cause and effect. They habitually behave on impulse, hunch, emotion. Conversely, we admire the scientist,

the executive, the military leader whose mind visualizes the
conditions of a situation and, as if looking at a map, picks out
the one logical course through the maze. It is something of
this faculty of logical thought that experts have been able to
build into certain specialized machines.

The mathematics of logic, upon which such machines work,
was originated a century ago by an obscure Englishman named
George Boole. This discipline, now called Boolean Algebra,
has proved to be of great service to telephone engineers in
designing automatic switching apparatus. Shannon and his colleagues D. M. McCallum and J. B. Smith wondered if they
could build a machine that would solve a variety of logical
problems other than those met with in telephony. They succeeded. Here is the kind of problem the machine can whisk
through in a fraction of a second:

It is known that salesmen always tell the truth and engineers always tell lies. G and E are salesmen. C states that D is an engineer.
A declares that B affirms that C asserts that D says that E insists that
F denies that G is a salesman. If A is an engineer, how many engineers are there?

Does anyone doubt that the human brain would have to do
some real thinking to solve that one?

Boolean algebra caught the eye of two Harvard undergradu-
ates, Kalin and Burkhart, some years ago and they built a
machine that would answer what appeared to be intricate
questions like this. They called their contraption the Logical
Truth Calculator. It created quite a stir in Cambridge because
it worked uncannily well. The problems it was good at were
the *if-then* syllogisms of rigorous logic. Not only *if-then* but
if-and-only-if, not, and, or and *or-else*. These are everyday con-
nectives which turn out to have quite a profound significance
in the life of the average person. You could not make up your
mind to do the simplest thing, even scratch your nose, without

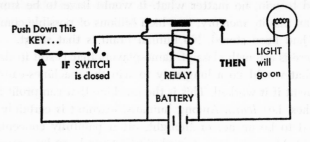

Push Down This
KEY...

IF SWITCH
is closed

RELAY

BATTERY

THEN

LIGHT
will
go on

Simple IF-THEN *circuit, using relay*

using one of them. "*If* I am thirsty, *then* I will get a drink
of—well, whatever I am thirsty for, *or else.*" Or the slightly more
innocent one, "*If* we had some ham, (*then*) we could have some
ham and eggs, *if* we had some eggs." The Kalin-Burkhart machine drew a lot of attention because the boys cooked the
thing up themselves, for $150 of their own money.

Next in line of sophistication came the machines that could
play games. Von Neumann and others have spent years studying the theory of games, and have written many books about it.
The mechanical game-players fall into a number of classes.
The simplest has a dictionary of rules in its memory, including
all possible moves to be made in answer to an opponent. A second class plays only according to a rigid formula, and can never
lose. A third category applies the principle of approximations,
choosing the probable best move by "thinking" over all conceivable moves and testing each against a criterion. The games
these machines can play include checkers, chess, bridge, poker
and many other card games. They can't always win because
an approximately right move isn't necessarily the *right* one.
But few human opponents can do better.

Only the simplest of these theoretically workable machines
have been built. Professor Wiener believes that a chess-machine
is possible, if it is built to look ahead only two moves. If it were

rigged to win, no matter what, it would have to be supplied with an infinite memory, in which billions of possible combinations had been stored. No human brain is that smart.

There is a fourth class of game-players that is still in debate, and that would go a long way to win the machines-can-think argument if it worked. This is the machine that can profit by its mistakes, i.e., *learn*. Among humans, learning is certainly considered to be an act of thought, often painfully concentrated thought. Machines have been built that can learn by experience and act upon what they have found out. Shannon breaks the problem down into four categories: machines that learn (1) by trial and error; (2) by imitation of a more successful opponent; (3) by being rewarded for right decisions and scolded for wrong ones; and (4) by figuring out the logic behind their mistakes and so correcting them.

Shannon and his colleague E. F. Moore built a machine to play the game known as "Hex," using an analogue computer working on electrical voltages. It beat them about 70 per cent of the time. "It frequently surprised its designers," Shannon comments, "by choosing odd-looking moves which, on analysis, proved sound." Thinking? Pretty close to it.

C. S. Strachey once programmed a game of checkers into a big computer and sat down to play the game out with it. His notes read like a humorous stream-of-consciousness story. About half way through, the machine had made several assinine plays and Strachey felt safe. He then made a careless blunder himself and the machine pounced on it at once. From then on Strachey was using all he had and the machine was still trouncing him. Finally, however, it weakened, and at the very end seemed to get tired and make purposeless moves, which eventually lost it the game. Strachey then did what few of us checker-players ever do: he set about seeing if he couldn't improve his opponent's game.

In all of these instances the machine is said to "learn" because it is so programmed that it follows the Boolean algebra format, discovering by sad experience that one thing or another doesn't work, and profiting by the mistake.

One of Shannon's more whimsical triumphs is the magnetized "mouse" which, when placed in a complicated maze consisting of partitions, is supposed to find the one and only path to the "cheese." On the first try the mouse will blunder aimlessly around, running into one wall after another. Eventually, by repeated trial and error, he will locate the cheese. However, if the mouse is given a second try he will go straight to the cheese without hitting a single partition or going up a single blind alley. He will do it from any part of the maze. Moreover, if his trainer changes the maze on him by relocating the partitions, mousey only blunders where the terrain has become unfamiliar. He can recognize at once portions that have not been changed. And when, at last, all possible changes of pattern have been foisted upon him, the mouse has learned enough to *forget* all of the former arrangements and remember only the latest successful one. The mouse himself does not think, but it is difficult to argue convincingly about the electromagnet and computer which drive him. The device does have the ability to distinguish between right and wrong, and to revise its standards upon the basis of its own experience.

Professor A. E. Oettinger has done similar work with the giant computer EDSAC in Cambridge, England. He "taught" the machine the useful knack of finding various items in a group of "stores," no one of which carried them all. The problem was for the machine to locate the store where a given item could be bought. After making all kinds of blunders, it eventually learned where every item could be had and would go to the right store at once. Then EDSAC was given a more sophisticated problem—to note the location of items it had *not* been sent to find. That is, it was asked to develop a certain amount of *curiosity*. The machine was able to do that too.

Another "learner" is the creation of D. W. Hagelbarger, a machine that matches pennies with a human opponent. This one attempts to find out whether the opposing player uses a system. As nearly everybody does gamble with some such scheme or pattern, the machine wins about 60 per cent of the time. Nobody, it might be noted, has developed a computer to break the banks at Las Vegas and Monte Carlo. Four scientists who thought they had a formula for it came home broke.

Samuel Butler, the great English author, took a prophetic view of the future world of machines in his novel Erewhon, published in 1872. Ever since, authors with less sense of satire than Butler's have envisioned horrible races of irresponsible mechanisms, turning the world into a shambles of slavery and death. In varying degrees, their imaginary monsters have been endowed with the faculty of reproduction, which permitted them to multiply until they could capture and crush humanity. These writers have made good reading, though nobody has really believed them.

Kurt Vonnegut, who used to work for the General Electric News Bureau, as I did, came out of it with a dour novel, Player Piano, in which he pictured all the routines of living as usurped by machines. His conclusion was that society would be divided between an aristocracy of engineers and an amorphous mass of workers with nothing to do but rake leaves. The machines attended to everything and would have run the earth if a bloody revolution had not stopped them.

Science today, instead of laughing at such extremes, is pursuing this very inquiry. Von Neumann, at the Institute for Advanced Study in Princeton, has carefully considered the question, Can machines become highly organized enough to reproduce themselves? His conclusion is that they may, provided they are complicated enough. Mathematically, there seems to be a bottom limit in complication that will permit reproduction. Below that, the iron mothers can only give birth to more primitive forms than themselves, and any "race" of inanimate monsters would soon lose the reproductive function. Above it . . .

If mathematicians are to be believed, we can rest fairly comfortably for a while yet. Human physiology is still millions of times more complex than Whirlwind or any of them. To duplicate the intricacies of the human brain alone would be a staggering problem. W. S. McCullough remarks that a computer with as many tubes as the brain has neurons would require the Empire State Building to contain it, Niagara Falls to power it, and the Niagara River to cool it. The use of transistors might reduce the super-giant to the size of a house

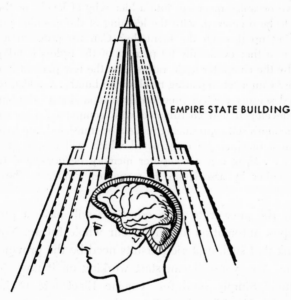

EMPIRE STATE BUILDING

THE HUMAN BRAIN

Two "computers"—the Empire State Building might be equivalent to the human brain in complexity only

and his power requirements to a few hundred kilowatts. Still, he would be a long way from the human brain, which will fit into a cereal bowl and takes about 25 watts of power. Then, too, complexity is not the only requirement. The billions of parts would all have to work together to produce reliable results. Considering how far from perfect most human brains are, there isn't much threat from a synthetic one achieved by even the best of them.

Rather than threat, there is a note of tremendous inspiration in these studies. "The problem of how the brain works," says Shannon, "and how machines may be designed to simulate its activity, is surely one of the most important and difficult facing current science." Greatly inspired himself, he cries:

Can we organize machines into a hierarchy of levels, as the brain appears to be organized, with the learning of the machine gradually progressing up through the hierarchy? Can we program a digital computer so that eventually 99 percent of the orders it follows are written by the computer itself, rather than the few percent in current programs? Can a self-repairing machine be built? . . . Can manipulative and sensory devices functionally comparable to the hand and eye be developed and coordinated with computers? Can either of von Neumann's self-reproducing models be translated into hardware? . . . Can a machine be constructed which will design other machines? . . . How can a computer memory be organized to learn and remember by association, in a manner similar to the human brain?

Surely the answer to such questions will have a profound effect upon automation and upon our whole future. Nor must you think that such esoteric pursuits need be the province only of genius. You yourself can start working on it now, in your spare time! Simply send for "Geniac Electronic Brain Construction Kit No. 1," and put it together as you would a knockdown bookshelf. If you run into trouble with it, the Geniac Company (Edmund C. Berkeley and Associates of Newton,

Massachusetts) will sell you a correspondence course on giant brains and how to make them. Or, if this is too stiff, begin with an article by Albert G. Ingalls in the *Scientific American* for May, 1953. With a little wire and a few light bulbs and relays, it seems, you can have a lot of fun.

22 | TALL TALES

If you believe that it is a waste of time to puzzle over the question, Do machines think?, consider one or two of the applications that have already been made of computer intelligence. You can be assured that every bit of the experimenting done on these higher levels reflects back into practical achievements.

Probably the most astute of all the information machines presently at work is SAGE, the Socrates of military defense, under test at the Lincoln Laboratory in Bedford, Massachusetts. The word SAGE was concocted from "Semi-Automatic Ground Environment Machine," with the usual talent for picking words that had useful initials and that still mean something. But the words are, in this case, a strong understatement. SAGE can not only detect enemy objects of attack approaching the Eastern Seaboard. He can combine the data on them, gathered from dozens of observation points, send our defense equipment into action against them, and keep at it till every enemy ship and missile has "splashed."

SAGE knows all. You would not be able to come into or go out of eastern Massachusetts by air without being observed by SAGE and his crew of Air Force specialists. If you were in the least suspicious, you would get a talking to in a hurry, for

SAGE would have snitched on you instantly. Even the New England birds are having trouble. If more than a few fly together in a flock, SAGE is aware of it, and has to be told to lay off; they are harmless.

SAGE is, basically, a computer in the true sense that he does computations, but he has every ounce of intelligence it is possible to load into a computer today. He is a data-processing machine *and* a machine of logic. He can well-nigh think. Of course, he has a simple one-track mind like his brothers and sisters. He is interested only in things flying through the air. He is like a huge guard dog that is constantly bringing quarry to his master for inspection. A nod and he chews it up; a shake of the head and he is no longer interested.

SAGE is a creation of the Massachusetts Institute of Technology and of the specialists of the Air Force, the brilliant work of Dr. Jay Forrester and of many associates. Under a secrecy blanket rivaling that of the wartime atomic bomb, the project has been cooking, under the designation "Project Lincoln," for a good many years now. The mere careless mention of the words would have been apt to get you the raised official eyebrow. Your best friends would not tell you what it was all about. An old and intimate scientific buddy of mine, who is nearly all brain, was involved in the project. I could not even go to lunch with him; he treated me like a stranger. Such care must mean that the secret is big. How big, we are allowed to have only a smattering of an idea today.

In general, this is what SAGE does. A small group of specially trained Air Force personnel sits in a big room completely filled with consoles and television screens. Dotted over the countryside of the region, radars ceaselessly sweep the horizons for objects flying aloft. When such an object is picked up, its image is brought directly to the screens in this control room. The numerous radars have triangulated on it and have given it a "fix." You see it superimposed on a map of the area.

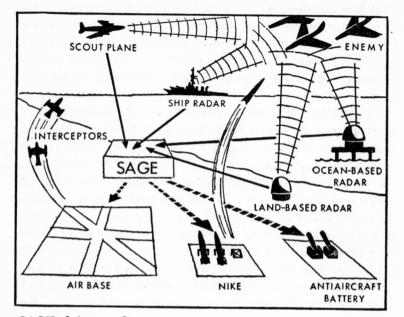

SAGE *defense scheme*

The work of "tracking" now begins. SAGE starts to grind internally in a jam-packed room adjoining the control quarters. In a few seconds, the computer has figured out the course, speed and altitude of the intruder, and this information is translated into lines of light and photographed upon the TV screens.

The control men have before them banks of pushbuttons, and with these they pose various questions to SAGE, filling in on the enemy till they really know all about him. They can also give SAGE such data as he needs. One such item would be that the offending plane looks like the four o'clock flight from New York. SAGE is asked to look up this flight and see if the commercial plane should be in this position at this moment. The computer searches its memory, in which all flight plans for legitimate aircraft are on file. He then comes back to the questioner, maybe with something like this: "Eastern Airlines has a plane from New York that was due 20 minutes ago at the observed location. Is this the plane?" This wordy bit of conversation, of course, appears in terse letters and numerals.

Now it is up to personnel to make the decision. They consult subsidiary data, which may be stored in auxiliary parts of SAGE's memory, telling them that on this particular afternoon the Eastern flight was late leaving New York, or had head winds on the way up. If the UFO (unidentified flying object) seems to fit the description beyond reasonable doubt, they can say to SAGE, "Relax. It's the Eastern flight." SAGE acknowledges by printing a letter F on the screen next to the slowly moving "pip" symbolizing the plane. That means "friend."

Routinewise, this goes on night and day all the time. And so far, fortunately, nothing has happened to mar the tranquility of the act. Nothing unexpected, that is. SAGE is continually being tested, against the time when a real enemy may appear. The tests consist of sending aloft target planes that will be treated as enemies in a series of war games. The computer finds them the instant they appear within his range of many hundreds of miles. He announces to his colleagues that these are probably not friends but enemies. They check and agree. He marks their images on the screens with flight data, and the chase is on.

Now comes the fun. SAGE, in a matter of seconds, has worked out the probable enemy course and where it will be best to join battle. He can decide, for example, whether an intercept by our fighters is indicated, and from what airport they should take off; or whether the enemy is heading in over one of our anti-aircraft batteries, or if the ubiquitous guided missile, NIKE, should be used. SAGE's reasoning is based on how to get those enemy objects out of the sky in the quickest and most effective way.

A swift O.K. to him and he then splits the job up among all

the enemy planes, following each one individually if necessary, computing the significant data on each simultaneously. Thus, the various officers and men in the control room can co-ordinate the battle and divide it up into individual fights if this is most efficient. The senior director, at his screen and console, can direct the whole battle or "sit in" on any part of it.

Now comes the battle itself. For this one, let us say, SAGE has decided to use fighter planes. On the screens of the Weapons Officer and his assistants, then, appears SAGE's roundup of instructions, based on the known performance and armament of our fighters. One of these men picks up a phone, connects through direct to the airport designated, and relays the information SAGE has given. In a jiffy the fighters are in the air with full instructions. So far, from the time the enemy was sighted, about two minutes have elapsed. How much longer it would have taken by the older method, using only human brains, is a secret. Enough longer, one presumes, to have made the probable damage from attack too large to be borne.

SAGE is by no means through at this stage of the battle. He is watching it minute by minute. Every change in enemy pattern, every evasive action, every kill, he records, and changes his tactics accordingly. Through Weapons Control he keeps up a running fire of instructions to the pilots aloft.

SAGE is experimental so far. A carping critic might say that he is not very bright, for he stops with instructions. But his descendants, already on the way, will outdo him. They will be able to take complete charge of our planes, once in the air, fly them, maneuver them, fire their armaments. These young mechanical geniuses, now in the works at the factories of IBM, will eventually dot the entire continent of North America, and make it very hard indeed for any unauthorized person to use the air for anything except to breathe.

And when the battle is over and all the enemies are "splashed," one will be able to imagine the personnel going in to SAGE and shaking his hand. "Good work, old fellow, you didn't miss a round!" they will say. For reasons of morale, there might even be a hand to shake, at that.

Exhausted now, let us retire into the peaceful confines of the library, where, believe it or not, something quite as exciting in computers-that-almost-think is going on. That is to say, a machine that translates one language into another. For some years now the drive to knit the world into a single fabric of permanent peace has been running parallel with high-pressure military efforts like SAGE. Both activities are essential, for the cold war has been continuously fought on the peace front, too.

One of the most unfortunate retarding forces against real peace has been the barrier of language. There are linguists who can surmount these barriers, but the everyday agricultural expert, doctor, engineer and business representative finds himself hopelessly slowed down in many foreign countries by his inability to communicate with any but the highly educated.

Nowhere is this barrier more keenly deplored than among the scientists themselves. While nearly all may read one foreign language, and sometimes speak it fluently, very few ever publish reports of their work in any but their native tongue. The result is that all over the world the sharing of discoveries is seriously impeded, and with it One World of peace is held back. Much significant work is repeated in different countries because of this failure in communication.

Some years ago, electronics engineers made a wild guess that eventually it might be possible to build a computer that would "read" a printed page in one language and deliver it, in type, in another. It was so wild a hope that many experts laughed at it. Norbert Wiener himself called it "unlikely." But a small core of forward-looking investigators, mainly in college language departments, pushed doggedly ahead into a formal study of the problem. It can now be said that a machine *has* translated material from Russian into English, well enough so that English-speaking scientists could gauge the importance of the Russian text.

The experiment was staged by the Institute of Languages and Linguistics of Georgetown University, with the co-operation of IBM. A standard 701 general-purpose computer was used. Heart of the programming scheme was the Russian-English "dictionary" of 250 words, prepared in advance and set up in code in the computer's memory. The experiment was a modest one, for the effort of coding was more important than the translation. Yet the basic principle was there, and was proved sound. The general scheme was to supply the memory not only with each Russian word and its English equivalent (sometimes several of them), but in addition, a number of different *word endings*. The memory was also given six basic rules of syntax, or grammar. The machine was asked to choose which of many meanings a word might have by the device of investigating related words around it. Special programming rules guided the computer in translating, in the light of these juxtapositions.

Although the demonstration could hardly fail, on account of its simplicity, it did prove that translation, in theory, is within the scope of mechanical brains. Basically, the problem was one of information handling, although to do a reasonably good job with a large vocabulary would require astronomical amounts of input data.

Energy for pursuing the goal of machine translation stemmed largely from Dr. Warren Weaver, of the Rockefeller Foundation, and Dr. A. D. Booth, of London University. As far back as 1946, the two began corresponding about it. Booth, who headed the Birkenhead Computation Laboratory, was sanguine from the first. So was Weaver. "It is very tempting," the latter wrote to Wiener, "to say that a book written in Chinese is simply a book written in English, which was coded into the

(*From M.I.T. photo*)

Russian-English translation as seen on Whirlwind's analogue display screen

Chinese code." Enemy ciphers had been regularly broken by computers during the war, he contended. Why not language ciphers in peacetime?

After the Georgetown demonstration in January, 1954, Weaver, Booth, Dr. William N. Locke, head of M.I.T.'s Language Department, and others started a Society for Machine Translation, and a magazine to give it a forum. They are in the thick of this now. In fact, there is an M.I.T. machine-translation team at work, using Whirlwind. If you ask Dr. Locke what he thinks of the chances of building MATRA, the mechanical wizard who can read Afghan and speak Greek in the same breath—a stunt done every day by human translators in the UN—he will smile and remind you of the problems to be solved first. The worst, Locke will tell you, is the incredible difficulty of transforming the syntax, or sentence structure, of one language into that of another. This will require a "dictionary" of enormous size. Webster's Unabridged contains some 500,000 words, each with several alternate forms, each verb with many tenses. Words with identical spelling may mean two or three or even more unrelated things. Millions of word-forms in all.

He will remind you, too, that English is not the only offender in this regard, but will add jokingly that Chinese would be one of the easiest to break down by machine, since it has no cases or tenses. Then he will point out that the words alone aren't the whole story. Word *order* is important, and very different in different tongues. Is the machine to rearrange a sentence seen in German, for instance, so that the verbs are picked up from the ends of the sentences and transplanted into the middle? You must have, plainly, a fantastic set of rules for each pair of languages, and if you tried to make a machine universal, able to translate any one tongue into any other, you might be encroaching on the complexity of the human brain. Nevertheless, Locke appears to think it can be done, even though a machine for general translation might be so expensive that only the government could own and operate it.

Running parallel with this gigantic problem in machines that think they think, is the whole question of communication in all forms—written and spoken language, music, TV, perhaps even art. The remarkable Information Theory, founded on Wiener's cybernetics and developed mathematically by Shannon, underlies the whole matter. We have hardly begun the application of it. The supremely difficult task that machines must master, if automation is to exploit its full promise, is our everyday use of communications media. So far, computers talk their own idiot language. They have got to be taught to talk ours.

The Bell Telephone Laboratories, which include Shannon, are far ahead of everyone else in their mastery of communication techniques, and already have a device called the "Vocoder," which listens to speech and "compresses" it into its essentials for highly economical code transmission. At the other end of the line it puts the signals through a "hiss-and-buzz" generator, which provides the raw sound materials out of which intelligible talk is made. The gadget doesn't speak elegant English, but a muffled hodgepodge as if it were talking under a blanket. But it can be understood.

Bell also has invented AUDREY, another of those mechanical girl-friends whose initials happily spell a feminine name. "Automatic Digit Recognizer" is all AUDREY stands for. However, she can listen to numbers and repeat them, and has learned to recognize 16 of the principal phonetic sounds. With the aid of a hiss-and-buzz generator, she can repeat them tolerably well. Like some humans of the same sex, she can't or won't recognize a woman's voice. She responds only to men.

You may ask, Why AUDREY in a world full of recordings and microphones? The answer is that once she has learned to listen and talk, she can send 100 times as many conversations over a telephone line as you and I can. AUDREY might fit handsomely into the mechanical translation scheme. She would make an admirable "secretary" who could listen to a book read aloud in one language and pass it on to a computer as a compressed code. This would solve one of the meanest problems, which is how to get a machine to read print. Of course, somebody would have to read to AUDREY, so she is not the final answer. That will come with the even more sophisticated mechanical ability to read print.

This art of reading has already progressed a long way. We have seen ERMA do it in an elementary way, with figures. There are machines on the market which can actually read a few kinds of printed letters and figures, and code them for later printing out elsewhere. The talent is called "character recognition"; a number of laboratories are working on it, perhaps the most advanced being the Intelligent Machines Research Corporation, in Arlington, Virginia. Character reading is done by scanning the material with a photoelectric cell and distinguishing the unique pattern which each letter offers,

(*Stanford Research Institute*)

Character recognition (the lower figures represent wave forms generated when the machine scans the figures with a photoelectric cell)

translating it into a wave-form intelligible to a computer. Not only is this important to banks and business houses for sorting documents. Over the horizon is the vast field of reading letters and documents in order to digest their contents and act upon them more swiftly than human beings can. Technical libraries are eying this development with much interest. If every book that came in could be read by an "intelligent machine," say in an hour, and reduced to digital gibberish on tape, a library could stack an immense number of books in little space, specially codified as to contents, and therefore more useful for quick reference. Perhaps, some day, publishers will issue special editions already coded by such a machine.

The Dutch Post Office uses one phase of character recognition to help in the accounting of its money orders. On the order form you find a printed box with two small shaded squares inside it, one above the other. The gulden amount of your remittance must be written into this box as a single figure in such a way as not to cross the shaded areas. Several boxes are provided for multiple-figure amounts. You will find that you can write any of the digits from 0 to 9 by circumnavigating the shaded squares. It gives a homely figure but one that a character-recognition scanner can read and tabulate at lightning speed.

These various coding schemes, ranging from recognizing a string of letters and digesting them all the way to MATRA, the Iron Lung of the Languages, are all for the purpose of removing the "platoons of girls" from the clerical bondage of routine reading and absorbing of sense of the written word. Now we should take a brief look at the other end of the line, the *de*coding end already mentioned, where the hieroglyphics carried in the computing machine have to be rendered into understandable form for humans to read. This is the headlong story of the high-speed printer.

A trip through an IBM factory would be a quick, though somewhat stupefying, way to see the printer at work. Here you will see rows and rows of such printers on test. Endless bands of paper are snaking out of them, covered solidly with letters and figures. The printing is a foot wide and contains 120 characters per line. It is being produced at the rate of 150 lines per minute. Try this on your typewriter. The world's fastest typist can do 149 words a minute. These robots are spewing out 3600 and making no mistakes.

At Remington-Rand there's a UNIVAC printer that does a trifle better. It gets out a paragraph of some 200 words in one second—the equivalent of a typed page. Somewhere within that second the machine has time to go over the whole thing and root out mistakes, too.

High-speed printing seems to me one of the most incredible achievements in the whole field of automation. How is it done? Only an electronics wizard could explain how, and I doubt if anyone outside in our worm-speed world could comprehend the explanation. Roughly what happens in the Rem-Rand machine is this: the continuous strip of paper rolls through the machine about as fast as a person's hand moves in washing a window. But the paper stops momentarily at every line, while the printer spreads as many as 130 characters on it, in a few tenths of a second.

Down inside the machine is a whirling drum, on which are embossed 51 rows of letters, figures, and spaces. Each separate row is devoted to one character, all A's in one, all 9's in another, arranged horizontally. The paper pauses long enough for the drum to make one complete revolution past it and hence expose to it all the characters. Now, a row of magnetically controlled hammers is poised behind the paper—130 of them, one for each character position in a line of print. As the drum rotates past the paper and the A row comes abreast of it, electronic coding actuates all the hammers that are to print A's in that line. That is, the a's in this line, three of them, would all get printed at the same instant, here and there across the line. A few milli-seconds later, the drum will have moved to present its row of B's, and a new pattern of electronically-actuated hammers strikes. So it goes, till the drum has made a complete revolution and all the character spaces have been filled in. All this, remember, has happened while the paper stood still momentarily. The letters print just as typewriter letters do, through a common inked ribbon.

In the tiny interval between the last row of characters on the drum and the reappearing row of A's, the paper is jerked along to the proper position for the next line. And so it goes on, for hours or days, if desired, as long as there is material on the coded reels to furnish copy. In describing this "printing on the fly" scheme, the engineers say modestly that they have had some trouble with sundries like carbons and ribbons. You can well imagine they might. However, the Thing will print carbons, up to four, just as well as it does single sheets.

You can hear the electrons laughing at this somewhat dazed explanation. They know well enough that when men's ingenuity has stretched a little farther, they will have to do much better still.

23 | THE MEN BEHIND IT

By now, the reader must have wondered how it is possible for any living brain to conceive such intricate things as computers and high-speed printers, and by sheer visualizing power, bring them down to practical hardware. It is a poignant commentary on the human race that it cannot solve its social and political problems, but that it can and does solve far more difficult ones in the realm of the natural sciences. One can only say that there is a special type of mind that thirsts for the disciplines of science, while there is no comparable clarity of logic and self-discipline in the field of everyday life.

What is this special type of scientific mind? And are we going to find enough of them to keep things going for automation at a time when engineers of any kind are in desperately short supply? First let us see what the requirements really are.

They break down into a number of classifications. There is, to begin with, the scientific thinker like Shannon, and behind him the wizard with logic like Wiener. Both, and many hundreds like them, are so tremendously driven by curiosity and a joyous spirit of exploration that they will go to any conceivable trouble to find out if a chance idea is valid or not. To the ordinary world it is often hard to see what these men accomplish. They seem to be playing games. There is von

Neumann, for instance, who spends years just figuring out what makes games playable. There is Wiener, who builds an intriguing little robot he calls a "dog" and studies its blundering antics as it wanders around the laboratory trying to find a goal he has set for it. And there is Shannon again, who is known to have asked all his friends to guess, letter by letter, a sentence he has in mind. Why? Because he suspected there would be a pattern in their answers which would throw new light on the science of information. If he asked enough friends to do it, he would see that pattern emerge. Shannon was magnificently right. There was a pattern, and the game was a definite contribution to his work on the Information Theory.

There is, after these, the type of man who can take a theory and visualize the practical applications of it to tasks which the human race wants done. These are not the Einsteins of science but the Bushes, the Van de Graaffs, the Oppenheimers, each of whom has visualized an actual machine or a system, reared upon the solid ground of scientific discovery. Such men bring the solutions to previously insoluble human problems. Men like these, in the early days, were the Edisons, the Thomsons, and the De Forests, the Jacquards, the Watts, the Galileis. We have them always—men whom the world thinks of as inventors, but who, in a broader sense, are the restless, eager thinkers who always want to do things better. Usually they have little thought of profit. Their game is a simple one: to outwit Nature and force her to yield new privileges to man.

Next in line come the practical designing and operating men, the engineers who go to school and learn methodically everything that has been done in their field, then go out and apply their knowledge by keeping our host of mechanical robots working. Eugene Ayres, whom I have mentioned, is, I assume, a man like that, in the oil-refining field. So was General Goethals, who built the Panama Canal. So have been tens of thousands of able, vigorous workers in applied science. Industry is full of them, yet it cries for more. They make up the majority of the men and women who graduate from our technical schools. They are the experts, the solid core of the engineering community.

Still another group in this indispensable army is composed of technicians—service men, maintenance men, highly skilled specialists in manufacture. Among them we find the operating personnel that keeps our huge mechanical plant running.

And finally, there is a vast, somewhat amorphous group, the business and economic leaders who command all the others and integrate their varied efforts into practical, useful, and workable products and services. Men like Admiral Ben Moreell, Alfred Sloan, Henry Kaiser, Henry Ford II, a host of others. This is the type of man today who must have more than just a talent for command. He must have knowledge of all the processes and discoveries he administers. He must understand science and its rigorous point of view; he must appreciate the public and its scattered loyalties and its caprices.

It is dangerous, I fully realize, to enumerate these various groups as though each were a separate and distinct entity. For many indeed are the men who cross the lines and function brilliantly in many fields. One cannot judge the worth of a man by the size of his individual contribution in his own field. It is a matter, rather, of how broadly his work is based on the common denominator of all fields, which is, in the end, the good of all the people. We are fortunate today, I think, that many have shown this broader competence; we are rapidly coming into a time when specialization will seriously reduce the value of the contribution a scientific man can make.

It would be fairly simple to blueprint the kind of men one needs to staff the field of automation and automatic computation, if it were not for the breakthrough which recently changed the outlook in this whole field. Here is a new art, with new theories and tremendous new tools which are mushrooming up so fast that it is extremely difficult to find specialists, even, who can function well in a single part of the field. Automation is not a technology that can be divided successfully into specialties. It is an intimate mixture of all engineering and scientific branches, inextricably woven with management, economics, labor relations, marketing. The expert who can effectively remodel an old plant or business into the streamlined organization of the future must be a composite of all of these. He has got to know a good deal about electronics, but not so much that electrical engineering is pushed aside. He has got to understand a lot of mathematics, but not so much as to push chemistry and physics into the discard. He has got to know business methods, and especially he has got to comprehend the statistical economics of integrating the operations of his firm. Otherwise he won't be able to understand automation and decide how much of it is wise. Above all, he must have an unbridled imagination, a vigor of mind commensurate with the challenges of the new day.

There are mighty few such men looking for jobs today. That is a potent reason why automation will not be upon us overnight, as too many people seem to fear. *There are not yet enough men to make it work.*

As an example, take the man who is to program a computer. Naturally, he must know enough about mathematics to feel at home in virtually any branch of that science, as it applies to a wide variety of practical problems. He must have at least a thorough groundwork in number theory and Information Theory to understand what a computer does, and what it ought to be able to do. He must be conversant with electronics and mechanics, enough at home with them at least to know the service techniques that apply to his machine. And he must have a very lively sense of invention, in order to see effective ways to break his problem down into computer language. Then, of course, he must know enough of the many branches of engineering to appreciate the problem itself.

We have been told that computers are able to program themselves, to some extent. Our programming expert must be able to take advantage of this and steadily improve on it. Otherwise he will not be forcing the machine to earn its keep. The common complaint that it takes months to program and minutes to solve is the nub of the whole thing. Is the human time justified? Are these brain-hours paying their way? A computer that costs $25,000 a month had better be kept pretty busy. Can its owner find men enough to keep it busy? And how will management know, with only the vaguest general understanding of the machines, when they have hired the right group of men?

The fact is, today, there are extremely few men to hire for this work of feeding computing machines. They are having to be trained on the job. Who is to train them? Who is to pick them out as trainable in the first place? When a young debutante was asked if she could play the violin, she answered brightly, "I really don't know. I never tried." This is all too likely to be the reply that a talent scout for computer technicians might get in his search for trainees today. Not a very promising prospect for a firm that has changed its whole business routine to fit around a million-dollar machine and must have the right people to run it.

Paul B. Wishart, of Minneapolis-Honeywell, said a while ago:

Already it is becoming apparent that the accelerated developments in science and engineering are pointing up the professional nature of the jobs of technical employees. Science and engineering are now so complex, and the technical decisions so specialized, that in many cases a whole course of business action is based on them.

Yet an engineer trained in one branch is becoming steadily less competent to evaluate the specific technical decisions of one of his subordinates whose specialty is in a different field. . . . The individual engineer is without question making management decisions, and must be counted as a representative of management just as truly as the manufacturing superintendent or the foreman is counted a member of management, because of the decisions he makes.

Automation is coming at a time when there is a famine of technical men of every kind. You read fantastic yarns in the daily press telling how companies battle each other in what *Life* calls the "flesh market for physicists"—not physicists only, but men of every discipline. Without technical people in abundance, our present way of life would collapse. The brave talk about expansion and a better standard of living all round is predicated wholly on the assumption that the chemists and metallurgists, the electronics men and the computer engineers, can be obtained in ever increasing numbers. If a shortage of skilled labor is threatening to curtail our upward progress, a shortage of trained technical brains will surely strangle it.

In this situation, what chance is there of inducing young engineering students, who see that they have things pretty much their own way anyhow, to take on the vastly demanding all-round disciplines of automation? Not much. What are we going to do about it?

The solution may lie, I think, in the group of brilliant men who stand at the root of the new movement—men like Shannon at Bell Labs, Gordon S. Brown and Jay Forrester at M.I.T., Aiken at Harvard, Harrington at Arthur D. Little, Inc., Groves at Remington-Rand, Watson at IBM, and a great many more whose names do not so often reach the public prints. These are, rather accurately, the George Washingtons of this Second Revolution, who will manage somehow to pull their forces through the Valley Forges of the new art and build a vigorous and long-lasting new edifice of science.

The outstanding quality they all have in common is their tremendous mental vigor. They are not bogged down in routine, nor concerned with personal security or pleasure or comfort. They are, in the hackneyed phrase, constantly forging ahead.

More, they are *accelerating.* As Newton pointed out, the interesting things in nature happen during the speeding-up process. Einstein showed that even gravity could be conceived as a type of acceleration. These men are the apostles of change, of progress, of motion. Out of mobility comes fertility and the energy to increase.

No one among them is more vigorous in the automation movement than Gordon Brown. He is an Australian engineer, with the drive of that pioneering country hot in his veins. As head of M.I.T.'s Electrical Engineering Department, he is probably as responsible as any other man anywhere for the successful solution of involved automatic control. But his energy is as much in his teachings as in his diagrams. "What we need is a dynamic society," he insists. "People want more; they won't get it along present lines." Automation, he says frankly, is the only way. But how? Through the building of a new kind of young man, possessing the broad training and the bubbling energy to bring about a dynamic society.

"Technical education is education in change," Brown goes on. "Up-to-date training means exposing young people to a creative environment. Creativity in science means that after you have uncovered a new piece of knowledge you must go on to new ground. The right environment for good training is on the frontier. Especially the military frontier."

At Project Lincoln, which developed SAGE and many other phases of our latest weapons program, it would be impossible to proceed rapidly without the help of advanced students in physics and engineering. There is a dilemma there, since the whole thing is top secret. Students cannot normally participate. When the problem came up, the Air Force and M.I.T. faced it and solved it immediately. Let the young fellows in, was the decision. Clear them, charge them with the responsibility of keeping their mouths shut, and make them a part of this pioneering work in automation that may be the secret of national survival tomorrow.

Under such training does a young man learn only the narrow facts of computer mathematics and electronics? By no means. He acquires something of the spirit. He learns that the one outstanding right in a dynamic society is the *right to risk*. He learns that one of the great requirements of all progress is that its leaders must develop the habit of curiosity. He discovers that elusive scientific term, *serendipity*.

Now here is a word you won't find in any but the largest dictionaries. It sounds like something out of an obscure corner of *Alice in Wonderland*. In essence, it *is* in the Lewis Carroll mode. Carroll, be it remembered, was a mathematician. Serendipity, though he never called it that, was a mainstay of his, and especially a mainstay of Alice's. Science is using it today as the basis for the expenditure of hundreds of millions in basic research.

It was Horace Walpole who coined the word over 200 years ago. He took it from an ancient legend which tells of the adventures of the three princes of Serendip. "As their Highnesses traveled," says Walpole, "they were always making discoveries, by accident or sagacity, of things they were not in quest of."

In the year 1900, Willis R. Whitney, a young chemist, established the first industrial laboratory in America, at General Electric. Whitney's whole basis was serendipity. His method was to hire men with big imaginations and good training, give them equipment and freedom, and let them see what they could find. He was gambling on the faculty of *observation*. Tremendous things have come out of that laboratory: the modern electric light, X-rays for medical and industrial uses, diathermy, artificial weather-making, basic discoveries in plastics, the artificial diamond, many more. The idea of financing serendipity spread through the industrial community. Today,

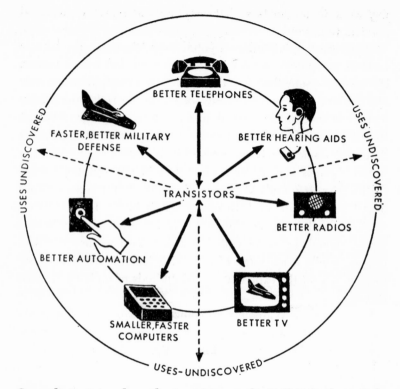

Serendipity turned up the transistor at the Bell Telephone Laboratories—see what has happened already

no large company dares be without it, and countless small ones are formed simply to exploit it.

It was a prime example of serendipity when Alexander Fleming discovered penicillin; another when Frederick Banting found the key to insulin. In Fleming's case, an unknown mold blew in through his laboratory window and upset a painstaking experiment. He dropped the experiment and investigated the mold instead. He knew that he was in the presence of one of nature's great disclosures. Roentgen went through the same process with X-rays. So did Bell with the germ of the telephone. Edison was doing it all the time—in outstanding fashion when he discovered the principle of the photoelectric cell.

Thus serendipity is not a whimsical word, but a rock-bottom principle of all modern investigation. It is a mainstay of science and particularly of automation. Now, the Browns and Aikens in that field have discovered that it must be the keynote for the training of the new engineer. What they are trying to turn out is the vigorous, alive, chance-taking young man who welcomes uncertainty, who turns an odd stone over just to see what is beneath it, who joyously assumes that nature has more to give and that therefore he must always be on the lookout for it.

These are the young men who will march in this campaign against too-little and too-slow. It seems to me, as it obviously does to Gordon Brown and his colleagues, that once our youth understands the challenge and the magnificent vistas of conquest that lie ahead on the frontiers, they will flock to the cause.

24 | IS THIS A TIME FOR LEISURE?

It is against the backdrop of serendipity and the great vigor of the scientists that the vast majority of us, employed in subordinate capacities, must evaluate our problem with automation. We have no more chance of stopping the advance of the new art than the pony riders of the Plains had of stopping Morse's telegraph. *We must grow up with it.* Here is a new treasure-house of science, rapidly opening at the hand of the pioneers. The average citizen has a place, a vital place, in the job. He can accept it eagerly, or he can allow himself to be left behind, a sacrifice to his own short-sightedness. Can he safely preoccupy himself with leisure at a time like this?

Although the change will powerfully influence us all, it has special significance for the men and women who work in office and industry. It is at the desk and workbench that the practical changes of automation will most strongly be felt. Since these working groups are, on the whole, well organized to promote their interests, automation becomes their serious official concern. Leaders in all fields today believe that the creative and far-sighted thing for the labor unions to do now is to look at their situation objectively and ask themselves what is likely to be to their best long-term advantage in the next few decades. Never, agree the authorities, has there been such a golden opportunity for the workingman to improve his social and intellectual place in the scheme of things. To do so, however, he must give the same frank and searching analysis to the situation as the technical man habitually gives to the intricate problems of nature. Purely emotional solutions can only bring trouble to everyone.

Automation seems to generate at once the extremes of fear and of inspiration. Extravagant worries constantly combat equally excessive claims for a utopia of ease and leisure. Many people, intently engaged on the scientific frontier, tend to brush human problems aside; many others, equally involved in the human problems of everyday work, let themselves go to pessimistic limits and thereby become too vociferous in defending the supposed rights of one segment of the people. The problems of a great social and technical change will be solved no better by the cry that no one must be hurt, than by the insistence that there is no human problem at all. My plea in this chapter, then, is for sober thought—careful and dispassionate evaluation of the problem of man confronted by machines which he must master before they master him.

The labor leader and politician who promise to see that automation is "controlled" are offering something they cannot deliver. A general would be as foolish if he contracted with his men to prevent them from being shot and killed on Sundays in an open war. The industrialist who categorically states that no one will lose his job when automatic machinery takes over, is prophesying beyond his ability. None of them appreciates the magnitude of the change. It is not a good time for us to listen to conventional assurances from unqualified guides, for the simple reason that no one *can* be qualified to state what will surely happen in the coming years. The best we can do is to inform ourselves to the limit on the conditions and to remind ourselves that the happiest and most productive member of the community is he who is best fortified with knowledge and understanding.

If we who work, then, at machines and desks, in the mines, behind the counters of stores and the wheels of trucks and buses, are to be forced into this new mould, what can we do to prepare ourselves for the transition? The one and only intelligent answer seems to be self-education. By this term I do not mean merely the learning of new and more skilled trades. I mean a study, through reading and discussion, of the broad factors, the very broad factors such as economics and technology itself. The main thing is not the detail; it is the spirit in which automation has been conceived. The important thing to understand is the irresistible force of science, as exemplified by such men as Shannon and Brown. The vital thing is to realize that they and their colleagues *must* make discoveries, and that the discoveries, once made, *must* change the world. We have no choice but to orient ourselves to their mode of thought, a mode in which men are no longer to be slaves to machines but masters of machines.

Let no one be stampeded by loose talk of a "Second Industrial Revolution" in which automation will sweep over us like a forest fire. Great technical advances do not come that way. Business is far too careful of its money to rush into an untried field overnight. And even if it chose to risk the money, it could not get the technical men needed to push the change through at once. Men as well as machines must be created. The worker who fears that automation will engulf him can, with very moderate study of current writings, and of history, convince himself that this "revolution" is for his children more than for himself.

Next, let all of us who work in industry, whether it be in manufacture or in office duties, look about with the same kind of curiosity the automation engineers use, to see what's in the wind, technically. I don't mean a technical study, of course, but a general spirit of alertness aimed at an understanding of the trend. What will such an attitude yield? At least, some appreciation of the reasons why automation is being adopted. At least some protection against surprise. To be forewarned is never a waste of time.

Third, it seems to me that anybody holding a job in a company where change is imminent, must see the wisdom of training himself, at least a little, to meet the change. Is there any doubt of the good reception a man would get who went to his boss and asked for help in studying up for a better job? There was that other Brown, Marcus by name, a truck driver for the Mount Wilson Observatory, who heard that a new telescope was to be built on Palomar. He went to the astronomers and asked if he might be trained in the shaping of glass. The making of a 17-foot mirror excited him. The management seized upon him enthusiastically, and Marcus Brown was eventually put in charge of the whole grinding and polishing operation.

There is a little of Marcus Brown hidden in us all.

Everyone who is concerned with bringing automation to pass is saying the same thing today: Training! Training early and well for the new jobs ahead. For example, the thousands of employees of the Bank of America must know by now that ERMA and her descendants are going to make a vast difference in the work-structure of the company. If they have studied the matter at all, they will understand that to expand, the bank must have this new automatic machinery. They will know, too, that the ERMA's of the future can't work alone. They require skilled operators and highly competent service men. So do the mechanical check-sorters and check-readers. Two choices are open to the employees now. Either they must be content to drop out when their old jobs vanish or they must plan to go on to better ones. These better jobs are bound to exist in ever increasing numbers. The time to begin training for them is at once. In every industry headed for automation, those who get in on the ground floor are sure to be the most secure.

There is no denying that many, for reasons beyond their control, such as age and limitations in health, may not be able to go on into the higher jobs in their present companies. A plant may close altogether; it may move; a different sex or type of worker may be needed. These are the people who will have to study the future most diligently, and face up to the change with the best compromise they can devise. In the vast majority of cases the employer will take care of them, providing training or opportunity in other work within their capabilities. The labor unions will assist in this and will care for the occasional hardship case that cannot be avoided.

The only folly that will lead us nowhere is the mistake of resistance, an attempt to pit our strength against the onward movement of automation. People who have tried to defy the great basic laws of change, since the beginning of history, have only hurt themselves. It has to be understood that automation is the expression of a forward-moving natural force, not the plaything of selfish men bent on private profit. The philosophy that automation is a new weapon in the so-called war between the classes will be less and less popular as we all come to realize the benefits of freedom from drudgery, brought about by better machines.

The signs are overwhelming that a period is coming in which there will be great shortages of workers in every field. How, then, can any of us fear technological unemployment? These fears, in general, are to be dispelled by a better understanding of our economic system than most of us have. Economics is a difficult, even an abstruse subject, but there are certain basic concepts which we should all comprehend. One of these is that productivity rather than earnings creates buying power. A second tells us that "wealth"—a high standard of living—cannot be had without work. In fact, that work is a

direct index of wealth. A loafing nation, or one that works in-
effectively, is never a wealthy one. Throughout human history
the vigorous peoples who have worked hard have risen above
their fellows, while the lazy have drifted into decline.

The largest share of the cost of any product is its work content. If we identify the items that make up the cost of a car,
for instance, we find first, direct labor, then materials and overhead. Breaking these last two down, we trace them finally to
other raw materials or services, which, in turn, are composed
mainly of work. The materials themselves were originally a
free gift from nature, to which has been added the work of
fabrication. Small fractions of cost have been assigned to taxes
—again mostly the payment for labor within government structures—and to profit, rarely more than 2 or 3 per cent of the total.
A small share goes for rental of the capital required to conduct
an enterprise; this rental is, in effect, a work charge paid to the
people who earned the money by previous work. It is in the
nature of a bonus for meritorious effort.

Automation will put greater and greater emphasis on machinery. The more and better machinery we have, the greater
production and the greater wealth we can achieve, *provided*
that the necessary human contribution in brains and skill keeps
pace. Kurt Vonnegut, in *Player Piano*, draws a somber picture
of this country in the grip of machines which do everything,
with the help of a very small and select hierarchy of brilliant
engineers. Nothing in any study so far made by science suggests
that such a thing can ever occur. For one thing, Vonnegut does
not show us who invents the machines, who builds them, or who
keeps them in trim. Further, he shows us only industry, which,
indeed, is a minor part of national life, though a vital one.
Again, he skips an intermediate period in which all this mechanization must have been foisted on the people and he fails to
explain how such a slavery could have grown up without
resistance.

But there is one thing that *Player Piano* does indicate that should contain a warning. The book pictures all those who once worked as human operators of machines as drifting in idleness. It presents them as having almost unbroken leisure. But it does not suggest that anyone has improved that leisure. Instead, with nothing to do, men have sunk to pitiable levels of uselessness.

We should all think very carefully about the progressive reduction of our work-obligation as a nation, which it is claimed will result from mechanization. Just how much of the benefits of automation can we afford to withdraw from the economy by starving the machines? They will not work alone; they must have creative human brains behind them; they must be built by human hands; they must be serviced and repaired by human skill. To the extent that these contributions are withdrawn, the machines must lie idle, or not exist.

Labor leaders have repeatedly stated that they expect to see the four-day, 32-hour week as a result of widespread automation. Let us examine the economics of this. In order to cut down the work-week by 20 per cent (from five days to four), it will be necessary to increase productivity by that same 20 per cent in order to retain the same output we have now. But we are in a period of strong expansion in demand. There must be, say the economists, as much as 40 per cent more goods in the next ten years. To produce them in the shorter work-time, then, it will require 48 per cent more productivity. It has been shown conclusively that no such expansion is in sight through automation. Nor is it in sight through foreseeable additions to the work force. Fourteen per cent more workers, we are authoritatively told, is the limit we can hope for. The four-day week, then, will mean *less* productivity by a large factor and a consequent lowering of wealth and standard of living.

Taken on a moral rather than an economic basis, drastic shortening of the work-obligation does not look too good either. Those affected—in industry—comprise no more than one-fourth of the total labor force, and not more than one-tenth of the total population. It is difficult to imagine a nation in which a sizable minority works briefly, while the rest work on as before. Most jobs cannot be closed down from Thursday night to Monday morning. Doctors' jobs, housewives' jobs, farmers' jobs, professional jobs of every kind—these must go on all the time.

Obviously, a complete cessation of productive activity for 43 per cent of our lives would be impossible, unless, of course, the work were spread so thin that everybody would do a little. That is, a general second shift that would also work four days, overlapping the first. Alternate shifts have been proved satisfactory in industry. Can they be applied to the other 75 per cent of our working force, and to professional activity as well? It seems to me extremely doubtful. Shall a dentist drop his instruments in the middle of a filling and relinquish the work to a colleague just coming on duty? Shall a minister preach a sermon but surrender the rest of his service to a second minister? Shall a teacher lay down his chalk in mid-line and summon a substitute?

These examples are absurd, we know. But they illustrate the folly of *discontinuity of effort*, which appears to be a real danger in a nation where effort must be integrated to the limit in order to support and enlarge productivity.

Again, and rather grimly, consider whether the machines themselves would tolerate a great disparity in work-contribution. As we have seen, any reduction in working hours must mean a very large increase in the number and effectiveness of machines and in the contribution of those who make the machines possible. This is tantamount to saying that the work burden will be shifted to a different sort of team—the team of human brains and mechanical muscles. If this change were forced to go too far, we might indeed get the very thing that Vonnegut envisioned—a busy aristocracy of brains and an unemployed mass of humanity whose usefulness was gone.

Undoubtedly, nothing like this will happen. I mention it only to show that we are playing with fire, where intelligent machines are concerned, and we cannot afford to ignore the principles on which a machine-backed society must run. The American people, as a whole, are a trusting and optimistic lot, and take much for granted. But there comes a time when inequalities are so obvious to them that they rebel. It was exactly such a situation that initiated the labor movement, and it was a healthy thing. Sweatshop owners were out of line; mass protest pushed them slowly back into line. Tomorrow, if labor assumes too great a share of the benefits of automation, automation itself will strike back at them.

Norbert Wiener has said that he is not greatly alarmed for the future. If we "go to hell," it will not be because we are too incompetent to avoid it, but because of some "accidental perturbation." In mathematics this means a sudden and transient anomaly, a brief act of apparent disobedience to the natural laws under which an activity is proceeding. In human affairs it means a violent upsurge of some one group, blindly striking out for its own ends. Hitler's rise was such a case; communism looks like another. It could happen again, in economics, but it is not very likely. There are too many checks and balances. Automation itself is apt to lure people on with better and better opportunities for an ordered, hard-working existence.

To round off this exploration, let us for a moment consider leisure. It is undoubtedly true that more and more of us will have more time for fun and relaxation. It is not quite so certain that added leisure will lead us to self-betterment. By and large, the people who work six, and even seven, days a week, seem to have the most time for reading, for discussion, for adult education, and for going to concerts and the theater. The mechanism here is plain: when the brain is fully employed it develops new vigor and thus demands more stimulation than when it is coasting along with little challenge and little time for exercise. The inference is that leisure is dangerous in a dynamic society unless the mind is first prepared by making useful contributions to the community.

An over-generous proportion of leisure could spell near-disaster if it were filled principally with more radio and unproductive amusement. A typical effect of having nothing to do is to do nothing. Not the least danger of such a course would be an unfavorable change in our comparison with Russia. In that country everyone is worked to the limit by a slave-driving state that permits no leisure and little self-determination. We, on the other hand, are going toward more self-determination and a great deal more leisure. We have no wish to create a slave state; it is against every principle of freedom and democracy. But, given the same mechanical tools, it is overwhelmingly dangerous to loaf in a world that contains a vigorous, aggressive and hard-working competitor.

A definite problem lies ahead in handling leisure wisely. It would be better for all concerned if we did not attempt to work less, but to become more ambitious instead. This I am certain can be done through education. The effect of this moral and intellectual advance, for one thing, would be richly reflected in the next generation. More ambition, more applicants for college training, more people capable of enjoying a better grade and degree of culture. A greater national virility.

The purpose of automation, socially, is the emancipation of millions of people from stultifying drudgery. Its purpose is not idleness. If idleness is the "perturbation" which results, automation itself will suffer, for idleness will rapidly strangle the supply of fresh and competent new brains. On the other hand, if leisure is devoted to real improvement of mind and spirit, there is practically no limit to the progress automation can make.

Too few of us have thought these things out clearly. Let us not make the mistake, in a dynamic world, of creating a vested interest in stagnation.

25 | SHALL I AUTOMATIZE MY PLANT?

The businessman today, especially the smaller one, has a difficult problem to solve with automation. Whether to get into it at once or whether to stay out; whether to devote management time and salaries to a study of the situation, or to hire outside assistance; whether to make a few cautious commitments in the new field or face a complete change, both in method and in product design—these are some of the tough decisions management must face. It is not easy to get sound advice.

The owner of a small company, say of 100 to 1000 employes, is in the most uncomfortable position, for his operation is big enough for automation yet too small to cushion the risks unless very solid assurances can be found that the gamble will turn out well. He reads extravagant claims for automation and reports of its fabulous success. He hears of labor's uneasiness and of the complicated situations that arise when the union insists on an overgenerous share of the benefits of the change. He gains the idea from some sources that automation is largely a matter of automatic control, yet from others he learns that mechanization is only a small part of it, and that to reap the real benefits he must turn his shop upside down and install everything, including an expensive computer. In his confusion, which is not his fault, he may decide to put the whole thing off, or at most

280

to delegate an engineering employe to the task of finding out what it is all about.

His dilemma is made worse by the knowledge that very large companies are marching ahead with automation, easily absorbing the capital outlay and the dislocations, and he wonders whether the market for his high-quality specialty may not be snatched away from him.

No one, of course, can decide but himself, with the best advice he can get. Before any decision is made, he will have to investigate the new field thoroughly. How is a busy executive to do this, and be sure of his information?

The first step, naturally, is to familiarize one's self with the meaning of automation and then make a careful survey of the business to determine whether automatic techniques will apply. There are many questions to be answered, and the danger is that the job will not be done on a broad enough base. There are so many degrees of automation, from small materials-handling machinery to over-all system mechanization, that some degree of automatic operation is applicable in almost any plant. If it is undertaken at all, however, the job should be done with the ultimate objective of complete automatization. Therefore, long-range planning, both of methods and of products, is an essential. Is the business expected to continue and to expand? Are its products looking forward to continually growing markets? Is mass production ever likely to figure into it? Is the company likely to pick up new products so different from the present ones that new types of manufacture and marketing will be needed? Most important of all, can adequate financing be arranged?

The financial outlook is a major factor in all automation planning. If the company's position is strong, it can easily procure the new capital needed. If it is weak, especially if it is weak because of too high manufacturing costs, capital may be more difficult to obtain, but automation may be all the more necessary to bring costs down. This factor may assist in getting capital that would otherwise be hard to obtain. In any case, automation is expensive and the savings flowing from it are not likely to be immediate.

In planning for automatic operation nothing is more important than the product itself. If it is fluid—a gas, a liquid, a continuous solid, or a single repetitive item that can be thought of as *flowing* through the plant—then continuous processing is applicable and automation will yield quick and often startling results. The same is true if the item is inherently suited to straight-line production—that is, if the product can be moved from one station to the next in a continuous and progressive set of manufacturing operations. A product such as shoes, for example. If it is neither, but requires many diverse operations, interspersed with a good deal of hand work, then product redesign must be included in the planning.

Furniture is a good example of the hard-to-automate product. A conventional wooden kitchen chair requires numerous hand-finishing steps and an assembly routine that would be extremely difficult for a machine to do. It would be a waste of time to try to automate this product as it stands. However, if the chair

(*General Electric Co.*)

Automation influences product design

is redesigned, say, to be made with seat and back of plastic and with legs of iron bent from one piece, then two straightforward automatic operations will produce the two subassemblies and a third will connect them and turn out the finished chair. Expected volume, of course, as well as analysis of customer acceptance, will have to determine whether or not to redesign and automate.

The tendency nowadays is to *think* a new product in terms of easy automatic production. We are surrounded by thousands of everyday items that have been "cleaned up" from the old, clumsy forms. Can openers, for instance, are now beautifully streamlined, enclosed, and finished in lively colors, with corners rounded off and proportions definitely aimed at eye-appeal. They are readily made by automatic means. Indeed, there are very few consumer products of the old-fashioned sort that cannot be redesigned to yield great improvement in cost and at the same time customer-appeal. It is fortunate that people nowadays expect streamlining, which fits so well into the automation picture.

An important factor to be evaluated at this point is the relative content of materials and labor. Often, more savings can be expected from a better choice of materials than from a cut in the direct man-hours of production time. Materials are usually cheaper when they are the result of the supplier's continuous production line, arriving at the plant in bulk. More important still, they are cheaper to handle.

Materials-handling is ideally suited to automation. Some of the most significant savings have been effected by cutting out the constant picking up and laying down of pieces of raw material. In smaller plants the chances are that all incoming materials are stored in the same area, with the result that some items must travel farther than others in order to be used. If the means of transfer are not up-to-date, there is much lost time and inefficiency. Hand trucks, small pick-up cranes, hand tote boxes and pallets, plain back-and-arm muscles are all of them expensive and slow because they require so much re-handling and shuffling of the items. Automation often makes it possible for incoming materials to be handled once upon un-loading, then not again at all.

Continuous conveyors are working their way into materials-handling in all automated plants, because most automatic ma-chines cannot be operated properly without them. While re-designing for automatic production, it is simple enough to carry the flow pattern for materials all the way back to the unloading platform. The greatest efficiency will result when the entire pro-duction process is integrated. The "black box" method does not work any better in a can-opener plant than it does in a military installation.

The question of factory buildings and floor space comes up early in all automation planning. Shall we begin all over again with new, modernized buildings? Or shall we try to adapt the present ones? The answer is to be found in the product and the particular form of automation suited to it. Most lately-built plants are of one story and have large open spaces that can be arranged and rearranged as automatic lines are put in. This does not mean, however, that older buildings of several stories may not lend themselves to modernization. It often happens that vertical transfer is very efficient, as in the candy plant, where the raw materials are delivered on the top floor. Here, all mixing and cooking is done. Intermediate products are then moved downward to the various processing areas by gravity. Packing and shipping are on the bottom floor. Conveyors today are so versatile that it makes little difference whether they move materials up, down, or across.

One thing that can be relied upon is that automation will take up far less floor space than present types of manufacture.

One of the most persistent worries that beset the businessman intent upon automation is the labor question. He does not really know what his obligation to his employes will be. Especially if his plant is unionized, he expects trouble. In large plants the union attitude toward automation may be a key factor; in smaller ones labor leadership is more apt to go along, since, on the whole, these men are much closer to the business and will understand more quickly the advantages of automatic operation. In either case, exploratory discussions with the leadership should certainly be held in order to size up the problems of displacement and retraining. It is essential that the workers be made to understand the economics of the change. Once they do understand, and are convinced that they too will benefit, their support is more likely to be gained.

Dr. Harrington mentions a case, in which he was a consultant, where the manufacturer employed 350 women. He wanted to automate, but was alarmed at the prospect of eliminating 23 of them. He felt an obligation to these girls and was fearful that he would involve himself in bad labor relations if they were let go. Harrington convinced him that this would not happen. A careful study of employment records showed that the normal average turnover among the women employed at the plant was close to 100 per cent every two years. Thus, while the automation lines were being installed, the employes would automatically decrease in number at a faster rate than the new machines would displace them. Actually, the employer would have to *hire* while he made the change-over, which he could do easily in conjunction with a retraining program. Turnover can be relied on to care for what somebody has called "girlpower displaced," and should always be taken into account in the labor phase of the long-range planning.

It is important, of course, that the employes understand the essential facts of automation, and in this respect the employer cannot begin too soon to educate them. He certainly has an obligation to his people to make their transition as smooth as possible and to avoid causing them hardship. This is not nearly so distasteful to management as many union leaders insist. There is a well-known case of a Midwest manufacturer who, on retiring his older men, sets them up in a small shop with the machines they are used to and allows them to make and sell whatever they want. Most plant managers are well aware of the increasing shortage of labor and of the need for upgrading that automation will bring. No one in his right mind would arbitrarily turn away experienced people who are already used to the plant and begin training strangers from the ground up.

These are some of the principal problems that the candidate for automation must face and solve, before he makes his final decision. Obviously, to make the shift a profitable one, the solutions must be arrived at with the greatest skill available. Too many small- and medium-sized businesses lack the technical personnel to handle it, and must look outside for help. In most cases the tendency seems to be to hire consultants to do the whole job. Until lately, such specialists have been hard to find. Today, they are rapidly increasing, especially among the larger companies which themselves make and sell automation equipment.

The job of analyzing a company's operations for automation is generally divided into two parts: *operations research* and *systems engineering*. In the field of office automatization, IBM offers a complete service, very expensive but also very exhaustive. For a large client like an insurance company, they will send in a team of engineers, accountants, and economists, who will spend a year or more studying every detail of the routine, management set-up and methods, plant locations, sales and even advertising problems. Such an analysis must be very thorough, and even though the client may not end up in the IBM fold, he will get great advantage out of the general recommendations resulting from the study. It is rather like going to your doctor for a general check-up.

Operations research is something new in engineering and not yet widely understood. It made its start in the late world war, on military problems. An outgrowth of it is the mysterious Rand Corporation in Santa Monica, California, where the Air Force maintains a large group of specialists of all kinds, who make over-all studies of future military aviation. Long-term research and planning, the Air Force has found, is the only way to be sure that the country will always be well defended.

Dr. Philip M. Morse, of M.I.T., one of the originators of operations research, gives this simple example of how it works. An O.R. expert was assigned to an Army camp to see how routine could be improved. On his first day he noted that there was a big line-up of men at the mess station after each meal. The men were waiting their turns to wash their kits in one tub of water and rinse them in another. There were four tubs in all, two for washing and two for rinsing. The expert watched the operation a while, holding a stop watch on it. He soon noted that it took a man three times as long to wash as to rinse his plate and cup. So he suggested to the commandant that three tubs be used for washing and one for rinsing. The change was made and the line-up disappeared.

Operations research, then, is the study of how an activity is done now and how it could be done tomorrow more effectively. It is not too different from the old practice of time-and-motion studies, except that it takes an over-all look for the purpose of building the entire operation for best terminal results. Very much in the same way as the Hoover Commission in Washington, it pitilessly analyzes every phase of the business and correlates it to the whole. It finds the weak spots, the repetitions and duplications, the "leaks" and faults in management procedure and structure. It writes, in effect, an idealized plan for the conduct of the business. If automation will effect improvements and increased profits, it will say so, and will locate the proper places to install it.

Say that a company does a million desk calculations a year, at an average cost of $30,000. O.R. men may suggest that an electronic data-processing machine could do the whole job for $30 or less (the figures are Dr. Forrester's). Aware that this is only the operating cost for this much work and that the computer's rental or capital cost would be enormous, they look around to see what else it might do if installed. Presumably they will find enough to keep it busy all the time. The machine can do calculations as much as a million times as fast as a man; it would be foolish not to analyze its utility across the whole span of the business.

Generally, operations-research groups themselves use info-machines to complete their studies. The beauty of the mechanical brain is that in the hands of experts, it can solve an enormous number of hypothetical cases with a single programming. Having established the variables that are involved in the business, and constructed a mathematical formula to relate them, the O.R. crew can, in effect, "operate the business" in facsimile inside the machine. In a few hours or days they can try out thousands of imaginary set-ups and pick the one for actual recommendation that shows the best results.

When the operations-research people have finished and their recommendations have been digested and a plan accepted, the systems-engineering group takes over. This is composed of mechanical and electronic specialists with the new, broad background of economics and management training. It is their job to turn the O.R. plan into hardware and into actual mechanized procedures. Like their predecessors, they are intent upon integrating all phases of the problem into a single unit, so that all parts will function in co-ordination. Everything is included, from the handling of raw materials to packaging and warehousing; from the first typed word on paper to the last.

This does not mean one vast machine, nor does it mean an "automatic factory." It merely means the best way to accomplish a task, in the light of all present engineering knowledge. An essential part of systems engineering is to anticipate the growth of the product through many changes, with the minimum of disruption and expense along the way. You will find systems engineers using computers in their planning, and building table-sized models of shop arrangements to illustrate the flow and work out the bugs.

For the first time in history, the businessman can begin to feel that his judgment will be backed by thoroughly reliable facts. For technical consultants today are ready and able to give him the same exhaustive planning service that the military receives in working out the national defense.

26 | WHERE DO YOU AND I FIT IN?

Without apologizing for the occasional "hard sledding" inevitable in a book of this kind, I will admit that it is not too clear where the average man will fit into the automation picture of tomorrow. As a matter of fact, we fit in on the ground floor, because if we don't get automation in the next ten years, we shall begin to notice shortages in familiar articles, and consequently sharp rises in prices. The general public always participates in a fundamental change of this kind, because it inevitably pays the bills. Who else is there to pay them?

Now, what are some of the advantages going to be? How are we to know that we are in the midst of this great advance, which seems to be understood and enjoyed only by engineers? Perhaps the last chapter of this book could risk a look into the near future, to try for an answer.

I believe you will notice automation first in the realm of prices. A very large number of homely, standard items will gradually become cheaper, as factories learn to make them automatically. Gasoline, electricity, and telephone service are three examples of early automation that have steadily reduced prices while virtually everything else has gone up. All of them cost today (aside from taxes) virtually the same in dollars and cents as they did 30 years ago, while the dollar itself has decayed miserably. This great net reduction in cost could not have been achieved without tremendous progress in automatic production. We shall undoubtedly see this same principle extended to many other consumer goods and services.

I believe that in everyday life you will see many subtle examples of automation working for the general good. In highway-traffic handling, for instance, the methods of operations analysis are making it possible to study traffic flow in a broad sense and with the help of computers to locate the bottlenecks. Electronic "cops" are going to appear at busy intersections and along stretches of heavily traveled highways. It will not be surprising if the insane jams we are used to now will be forgotten.

Everywhere there is going to be a clean-up in the sloppiness of doing things: less waiting in line in banks and railroad and bus stations; less annoyance and delay in travel; above all, fewer complications in paper work, such as in filing income-tax forms. This streamlining of paper routines will be tremendous. A great deal of the filling of forms, the reading of fine print, the distributing of multiple copies, will be gone. Mechanical filing systems will make much of it unnecessary. The point is under study now by lawyers as to whether documents on punch cards and magnetic tape are legal. Unquestionably they will be declared so, with a consequent great saving in the complexity of our relationships to each other.

You are going to know a lot more about the weather. I can imagine a railroad or airline obtaining an automatic prediction service from the Weather Bureau, which will enable them to offer you a guaranteed good-weather weekend or vacation in some chosen spot. They will "sell" you next month's weather along with your ticket to enjoy it.

You are going to get your mail faster and with fewer missent items. The Post Office Department even now is experimenting with info-machines to care for the staggering quantities of routine that human hands have to do now. A "digital mail sorter" is already in existence.

Your library is likely to be quite a different place. It has been estimated that the number of books doubles every 16 years. How would you like to have access, right in your own home town, to practically any book you wanted? Today that is impossible because of lack of space and of funds for purchasing books. Tomorrow it won't be, for there will be small cards on which entire books are printed, and home "readers" by which they can be enlarged for easy reading. Micro-books store so compactly and cost so much less to produce than standard books that almost any small library can have as many as it wants. Furthermore, an automated system will help you find, not only a good book to while away the time for pleasure, but the informative book, with just the material in it you are searching for (and today rarely find). Automated filing has tremendous importance in all research fields, where information hopelessly buried can be "dug out" by computer in the space of a few minutes.

Education is bound to be greatly affected by automation. People have got to know more and be quicker to catch on in a world where the human hand and brain are shifting their burdens to machines. *Everybody* will need more education. Professor Aiken sees the time when this shift toward better brains, better stocked, will keep large numbers of adults in training for most of their lives, following voluntary urges toward self-improvement.

Adult education, of course, will not be enough. We can expect important changes in college courses; we *must* expect better teaching and broader curricula in secondary schools. Many children today are still being trained for jobs that will not exist when they grow up—clerical as well as old-style artisan's jobs. A system like this is obviously expensive and wasteful and carries much potential grief for the young people, who have to take what is given them in school. It seems to me that to-morrow's education will be much more intelligently planned to fit into the dynamic society we are preparing. More science, more discipline, more of the future and less of the past.

The change will not be so much a question of material taught as of spirit. For our new world there must be the rediscovery of vigor, the preparation for change, the training for acceptance of opportunity and risk, the keening for exploration and pioneering. The objective will be to regain some of the spirit of daring that has been lost through the attitude of slavery to machines. Automation itself will, of course, require profound changes in technical education, reaching back into grade school, where its general principles will be taught. The core of the matter will be to learn to live in a world of machines and to out-think it and to control it. This transcends the sum of all engineering and penetrates deep into the field of philosophy.

People casually interested in a new thing always seem to wonder how it will affect their lives at home. I do not see any great change in home life through automation, except perhaps in the reduced cost of building a place to live. The building trades, for centuries embracing a kind of semi-artistic relation of worker to job, have remained so conservative, so reactionary, that today they seem downright archaic. More and more, I suppose, we shall see prefabrication, but on a more and more unstandardized basis. We may even see computers in use in architects' offices to assist in designing structures which exactly suit the client. In the meanwhile we are sure to see isolated examples of better ways to do the work of construction itself.

If one man can paint six different auto fenders in six different colors at once, why should it take three or four men several days to paint one house one color? Answer: one job is automated, the other is not. Automation will, in time, demand some sort of compromise in this. You can expect to see more and more automatic machinery on the job when you build.

I have already seen an automated nailing gun, much like a stapling tool. Held in one hand, it will "blow" nails into wood as fast as you can spot the places you want nailed up. It isn't likely that such a tool will come without a struggle, but it will be there, especially in the building of tract houses.

We cannot afford to underestimate the tremendous pressure of a broad public demand. There is no advantage to anyone in using slow hand methods which keep building costs at fantastically high levels, when mechanization would unloose a flood of desperately needed new housing and make steady work for thousands of artisans who now have to get along on partial employment. Work strangulation by the trades is an obsolete holdover from hand-work days, which cannot withstand the weight of automation pressure.

Lately, a General Electric official, Richard K. Fairley, did a little dreaming about the expected results of research "for better living." It was his thesis that research is bound to come up with startling new things in the way of automatic devices. He mentioned the transistor as a key to a whole new field of applications. Two hundred and fifty times smaller than the smallest vacuum tube, it takes up 1/2000th of a cubic inch of space, uses much less power, and costs less.

The company, he said, "plans to market a pocket-size transistor radio, hardly bigger than a key case." He went on to describe a future home in which the housewife "could brush her hand lightly on the alarm clock to turn it off, gently touch the top of the coffee-maker to turn it on, and merely place a utensil on the stove to start the burner heating. . . . There is apparently no limit to the horizons."

I can think of one or two limits: a tiny, kitchen-drawer-sized computer for planning menus. Every morning you simply punch buttons on its face that record inside what you have in the ice box. Punch a final button and a small screen displays a variety of menus you can make from the things on hand. Just like that.

And as far as alarm clocks go, Dad should have one, too, that will turn itself off when he wakes up and roars, *"Shut up!"*

One of the mightiest jobs for the mechanical brains of the future will be the exploitation of the mathematics of probability. Already, as Dr. Philip Morse points out, the theory of probability is the basis of operations research. It is also the key to the Wiener-Shannon Information Theory. Probability, of course, is an elusive genie that we would all like to have working for us. We may *say* that we want security, but the universal tendency to gamble, one way or another, is proof enough that there lurks in every human heart the passion for taking a chance. This is nothing more, really, than watching, fascinated, as the mathematics of probability goes through its paces.

Computers can do a great deal with statistical problems, and it can be shown that probability becomes near-certainty when enough statistics are known and operated upon. The fact that UNIVAC turned in an amazingly accurate prediction of the Eisenhower landslide of 1952, should point strongly to the kind of prognostication that computing machines will be doing for us tomorrow. How many personal problems can you think of that you wish you knew the answers to right now? Probably dozens. Most of them would be too trivial for expensive analysis, yet one can easily dream of a consultation center to which one could bring his problems and take away reliable answers.

Will there ever be a genuine automatic factory? I can find no one who believes so. There are already a few examples of nearly workerless plants—the dry-ice plant of the Union Carbide Company in Los Angeles, and the Rockford, Illinois, Army Ordnance factory for making shells. Neither is workerless, for there is always the need to load in raw materials at one end and remove finished products from the other. Also, there is maintenance. It takes an able, round-the-clock squad of men to keep an automated production line running. They must work fast, with high skill, for time out of production is expensive.

An automatic plant on the lines of Oliver Wendell Holmes's One-Hoss Shay would be good. The shay, you remember, went for 100 years and then fell apart, completely done-in in every detail. We shall not see machines or factories on this pattern. Man-made devices always have weak spots. Bearings do wear out faster than frames; vacuum tubes have definite life-spans. No factory will connect itself to an oil well to obtain fuel and lubrication. Someone has to be there to take a hand in emergencies.

We miss the point when we worry about robot factories that may run amuck. There is still that million-to-one advantage of the human brain over the mechanical one. The plant of tomorrow will turn out enormously increased production in relation to human *drudgery,* but it will never turn out as much as it does now in relation to human intelligence.

I don't believe that the workingman, once he gets by the stage of nervousness that his misconception of automation has induced, will find the situation anything but good. He will be in a far better position than he is in now, for he will stand very much closer to the product he is making, and through it, to the consumer for whom he is really working. Automation is, in a way, a return to the guild system, since it tends to make human beings responsible for an entire product rather than for a single spark plug in it.

Such responsibility will inevitably call for more intelligence, more *attack* upon the problems of life. I do not see breadlines; I see lines of applicants waiting at college registration offices. I do not see idleness, which creates no wealth, but keen attention to many jobs rather than to one stultifying job. The machines we have in prospect will not stand for poor-quality contributions from their masters. They will not, in the long run, stand for less work, but rather for more, of a better kind, more stimulating, more rewarding, better paid.

Utopia? Define it and perhaps we can predict the chances of

getting it. My vote would be against it. There is something sticky and sedentary about the utopias I have seen outlined. All of them are based upon perfect ease, perfect comfort, perfect *level*. Nature abhors a vacuum; even more, she abhors standing still. Like a baby, the new machine will be having us up at all hours tending to it. Like a baby, the new machine will endlessly suggest having more babies. The creative spirit, wherever it may be exercised, is one thing the human race cannot escape.

Our Utopia of automation will be, I am sure, an emancipation from the work of slaves that there may be more time and energy for the long climb that is ahead. The climb in human dignity, toward a better use for the human mind.

WANT TO READ MORE ABOUT AUTOMATION?

It would be difficult to pick up a newspaper today without finding some mention of automation or some expression of opinion
about it by a real or self-appointed expert. But these bits of
news reporting do not give much satisfaction nor do they help
greatly to an understanding of the subject. In this present book,
we have seen the broad panorama of what Dr. Gordon Brown
calls "a new way of life." For those who would like to go a little
further, the following references are suggested. You will soon
find, as you read them, that they lead forward, deeper and
deeper into the subject, one reference generating a dozen others.
Before you are through, you will be thoroughly automated
yourself.

In the way of books, try these:

John Diebold: *The Advent of the Automatic Factory.* Van Nos-
     trand, 1952.
     Not quite up to date, but still pretty much the pioneer text.
Norbert Wiener: *The Human Use of Human Beings.* Houghton
     Mifflin, 1950.
     Dr. Wiener himself explains that this book is a "popular
     translation" of his well-known work on cybernetics. It is full

of provocative ideas, perhaps not all stated with the consecutive clarity that the lay reader would appreciate. The book leaves you with the impression that you have been locked up in a room with a computer overnight. Still, the eager reader on automation is advised to go through *Human Beings* before trying *Cybernetics* (Wiley, 1948). The latter takes some mathematical courage.

Edmund C. Berkeley: *Giant Brains, or Machines That Think.* Wiley, 1949.

Like the others, a trifle behind the times. It is also a bit on the extreme side. But it is easier reading than the others.

B. V. Bowden (editor): *Faster Than Thought—A Symposium of Digital Computing Machines.* Pittman, 1953.

Twenty-four British experts explain the subject.

The Automation Handbook. Rimbach, 1955.

Everything in handbook form.

W. Sluckin: *Minds and Machines.* Penguin Books (no date given).

Another English contribution. The British scientists are apt to seem slightly more lucid than the American.

Wm. N. Locke (editor): *Machine Translation of Languages.* Wiley and M.I.T. Press, 1955.

Again, a symposium by experts. But you will find much fascination in this discussion of very-nearly-human computing machines.

Philip M. Morse and George E. Kimball: *Methods of Operations Research.* Wiley and M.I.T. Press, 1951.

The mathematics of the Theory of Probability, as it applies to engineering planning. Only for engineers.

In the way of magazine fare, this procedure is suggested:

Pick up almost any trade journal, especially in the electronics field, and you will find at least one article per issue on automation and automatic control. There are two magazines, so far, devoted to automation and automatic control exclusively: *Automation* and *Automatic Control*.

A really comprehensive bibliography of articles on automation would fill a large volume. Various authorities have compiled extensive lists of references. One of the most exhaustive, if somewhat slanted toward the labor side, was made up by Ted F. Silvey, National CIO Headquarters, Washington, D. C., and can be obtained by writing them. Another, slanted toward *library* automation, was compiled by Helen Loftus for the Lilly Research Laboratories, Eli Lilly & Co., Indianapolis, Indiana.

Copies of the *Readers Guide* and the *Industrial Arts Index*, on hand in most libraries, give complete listings of automation articles under the headings "Automation" and "Machines, Automatic."

INDEX

DATE DUE

GAYLORD 234   PRINTED IN U.S.A.

DATE DUE

GAYLORD 234   PRINTED IN U.S.A.